S0-BAB-825

Marie L. Hoegner

N.H. F ×/45

11/77

ANIMALS
OF THE
SEASHORE

BY

MURIEL LEWIN GUBERLET

BINFORDS & MORT, *Publishers*

PORTLAND, OREGON

COPYRIGHT, 1936, BY METROPOLITAN PRESS

*   *

Revised, corrected and re-printed in 1949

O what an endlesse worke have I in hand,
To count the seas abundant progeny,
Whose fruitfull seede farre passeth those in land,
And also those which wonne in th' azure sky?

SPENSER—*Faerie Queen*—BK. 4, CANTO 12

*Printed in the United States of America by
Metropolitan Press, Portland, Oregon*

PREFACE TO FIRST EDITION

THE purpose of this little book is to acquaint the nature lover with the common seashore animals of the Pacific Northwest. It does not attempt to give a comprehensive description of the species but mentions only such characteristics of each as are necessary for identification. There are notes on the habitat, size, color, food, respiration, movement, method of reproduction, and distinguishing characteristics. In addition to these facts about the species some general comments are made upon the habits of the class of animals to which the species belongs. These more general facts were gleaned from many sources and authors. It does not seem practical to give the references for all of them. As far as possible technical terms and difficult scientific names are omitted. Common names of seashore animals are not generally well established or are strictly local in use, so it was necessary to coin common names for a number of them. When this was done some behavior pattern or physical characteristic was incorporated in the name to make the name as logical and reasonable as possible.

There are, of course, more animals in this region than are listed in this book, but many of them are deep water forms that seldom or never appear on the beach. To secure the deep water species, it is necessary to use a boat, a dredge, or other special equipment. No doubt, some animals have been omitted which should have been included and vice versa, but it is impossible to make a detailed study of every beach to discover possible variations. Differences between species are sometimes so minute and environmental conditions effect such changes that there is the possibility of discrepancy of detail between the descriptions and individual animals. However, if the book serves as a guide to identification, it will have fulfilled its mission. Further information about the animals may be secured from monographs and pamphlets written by specialists in the particular field or from the books listed in the bibliography of the present work.

The photographs which accompany the sketches should be as valuable for identification purposes as are the descriptions. Photographs of these invertebrates were, in most cases, taken from living specimens under water. Highly active animals were given an anaesthetic in order to quiet them before being photographed. Mr. Kelshaw Bonham deserves much credit for his patience and skill in doing this difficult photographic work. Without the aid and censorship of Dr. John E. Guberlet this little book would never have been written, for as a Professor of Zoology at the University of Washington and as a member of the staff of the Oceanograhpic Laboratories at Friday Harbor for many years he has acquired a wide and accurate knowledge of the seashore animals of the Northwest. Dr. Belle Stevens gave valuable assistance in the selection of Crustacea and in compiling facts for the sketches in this phylum. Thanks are also due to Prof. Trevor Kincaid and Dr. Robert C. Miller of the Department of Zoology and to Dr. Thomas G. Thompson, Director of the Oceanographic Laboratories at the University of Washington, for helpful suggestions and advice. Special acknowledgment should be made of that most valuable book *Seashore Animals of the Pacific Coast* by Johnson and Snook. It was referred to constantly and was of inestimable value in compiling the present work.   M. L. G.

Seattle, Wash., July 1936

PREFACE TO SECOND EDITION

It is a satisfaction to both author and publisher to find that *Animals of the Seashore* continues to meet such approval of persons interested in the animal life on Northwest beaches that a new edition has been made necessary.

Because most seashore animals are small and inconspicuous, because they do have well established common names, and because scientists have used difficult scientific terms in describing them; few persons know the animals of the seashore. It was to bring non technical information about the habits and life histories of these curious little creatures to casual seashore visitors and to owners of homes on the beaches that this hand book was written. It has served its purpose well.

During the years that have passed since the book was published, it has helped thousands of persons, both children and adults, to become acquainted with the animals commonly found on the beaches of the Pacific Northwest, and thus it has increased their pleasure in visiting the seashore.

It is also a satisfaction to the author to find that the original selection of animals was so carefully made that few additions are necessary in this edition. The animals described were mostly those found in the San Juan Archipelago. Recently Irma Rodenhouse, an enthusiastic and well-informed collector, has made an extensive survey of the animals living on the beaches of Vashon Island, the lower part of Puget Sound, and the ocean beaches of Oregon and Washington. Mrs. Rodenhouse found the seashore life in these regions almost identical with that of the northern beaches. However, she discovered a few species in comparatively large numbers in these areas which are not numerous on the San Juan shores. It seemed wise to include these in a revised edition of *Animals of the Seashore*.

Because of the expense involved and the small number of additions to be made, the publishers did not feel justified in making a complete revision of the book. Therefore it was decided to list the names of the animals in the preface of the second edition.

Most notable among these are: The sea anemone-*Meridium dianthus* Ellis; the white spaghetti like Echiurid or inn keeper worm (*sp?*)

which lives in a U-shaped tube; the bright red starfish-*Mediaster aequalis* Stimson; the large pink starfish-*Pisaster brevispines* (Stimson); the small, spiny, drab starfish-*Leptasterias groenlandica* (Lutken); the white cucumber with orange tentacles-*Eupentacta* (Cucumaria); *quinquesemita* (Selenka); the large thin shelled clam-*Macoma secta* (Conrad); a small species of the same clam with two indentations in the margin of the shell-*Macoma indentata* Carpenter; a small clam with a delicate pink exterior and a shiny salmon pink interior-*Tellina* (Morella); *salmonea* Carpenter, the fine checkered limpet-*Acmae persona* Eschscholtz; the cup and saucer limpet-*Crucibulum spinosum* (Sowerby); the isopod which rolls up like a pill-*Exosphaeroma oregonensis* (Dana); three crabs found in the shells of the horse clams, the geoducks, and the large mussels -*Fabia subquadrata* (Dana), *Pinnixia longipes* (Lockington), *Pinnixia faba* (Dana).

It is the hope of the author that *Animals of the Seashore* will help more and more persons to become acquainted with and to enjoy the densely-populated, fascinating natural realm—the seashore.

M. L. G.

Seattle, October, 1948.

INTRODUCTION

THE seashore may be defined as that narrow strip of land between the high and low water marks of the spring tide. "It is the haunt of a rich and varied group of animals and has, because of its unique position at the junction of the land and sea, an interest altogether out of proportion to its area." (*The Seashore*—Russell and Yonge.) The population of the seashore is one of the densest and most varied on the face of the earth. Even New York City with its restless millions and its welter of races and peoples does not have as many inhabitants as does a crowded seashore.

All animals must face and conquer certain conditions in order to live, and all have different ways of solving their problems. Some of the factors which determine the distribution of seashore animals are the type of beach—sandy, rocky, or muddy; the salinity and temperature of the water; the velocity of the currents; the quality and quantity of the food supply; and the power to escape from enemies. Most seashore animals are incapable of rapid movement and so require many special adaptations.

Our shores offer a unique opportunity for the study of marine animals. There are barren, rocky cliffs, stretches of sandy beach and muddy inlets, and each habitat presents its own problems and harbors its own dwellers. This diversity of shore line and the consequent range of physical conditions foster a vast number of species and individuals of shore animals.

In general, the rocky beaches and reefs have the greatest variety of animals. Here one has only to turn over a rock to see myriads of creatures hustle about in dismay. Some species hide in the crevices of the rocks while others cling to the rocks themselves. Starfish, ranging from three inches in diameter to those with an expanse of three feet, conceal themselves among the rocks. Barnacles, those jagged, ill-behaved little fellows who stand on their heads and kick food into their mouths, are omnipresent. Large, spiny sea urchins and slimy sea cucumbers add their exotic colorings and strange modes of life to the picture. Bustling about in perfect safety is the bold hermit crab. This animal appropriates the shell of a snail for his house and carries it about on his back until he outgrows it and then seeks a larger domicile.

An excellent cross section of the animals on a rocky shore is found in the tide pools which the outgoing tides leave in the hollows of the rocks.

The tide pools are natural aquaria which furnish endless pleasure to a nature lover. The bottom of the tide pool is often so encrusted with sponges or coralline algae that it looks as if it were splashed with red paint. A few small crabs and shrimps also give color to the pool. Within the pool live the flower-like anemones and dainty hydroids. Lying quietly on the bottom of the pool are sea cucumbers and tube worms with their bright red tentacles spread out to catch food particles in the water. On the edges of the pool cling limpets, chitons and snails, while the green urchins clad in spiny armour sit close by in bold defiance of danger. In and out swim beautiful, transparent jelly fish.

The sandy beach is inhabited by animals which burrow easily in the sand. In fact, the sands are as densely populated as is the surface. Each jet of water spurting out of the ground reveals the hiding place of a clam, while the lifting of a shovelful of sand discloses a whole community of worms. Crabs scuttle about on the wave-washed sands and countless amphipods and beach fleas hop in all directions. Queer egg cases of marine animals lie in profusion on sandy beaches. A strange sight is the "sand collar" which contains the eggs of the moon snail. Piles of cylindrical capsules sometimes called "sea corn" hold the eggs of the triton and the so called "devil's pocketbook" is the egg case of the skate. "Tracks in the sand mean as much to the seashore naturalist as do the tracks in the snow to the hunter or trails to an Indian." (Arnold).

Many animals live on the eel grass which grows abundantly on muddy shores. Snails, clams, mud crabs and worms hide themselves on mud flats. Especially beautiful is the delicate little snail, the wide chink, which deposits its eggs in tiny yellow rings resembling doughnuts. Many gaily colored nudibranchs live on the vegetation growing on the muddy shores. Mud flats are neither beautiful nor pleasant to stroll upon so they will probably not claim much of the collector's attention.

There is a constant struggle for existence on the seashore for the water is full of animals that prey upon one another. Warfare is deadly and continuous. Some one has said that the rule of the seashore is, "To eat and be eaten."

On every beach some animals are always present, some are usually found, and others only rarely occur. Physical conditions of the water, the season, and the winds may account for this variation. Of course, the greatest number of animals can be found when there is an extremely low tide, but many forms may be seen with average tides. An element of excitement always exists for the collector because no one knows what each day's search may reveal.

The student of nature should enjoy seeing and studying the animals in their natural habitats and should not carry home much of his find. It is almost impossible to keep marine animals alive under artificial conditions and our rich beach life should be as carefully conserved as are our wild flowers. To know and enjoy the fauna of the seashore requires no special equipment or knowledge of science. One needs only to form the habit of close observation and to see and note with a biologist's eye. Once the trick of observation has been acquired it is easy to read the signs on the beach. The study of seashore animals in their natural habitats is a fascinating pastime which more than compensates for the inconveniences one must suffer if he is to catch the low tide. Try it.

It is impossible to state with any certainty how many species of animals there are living on the earth, but Dr. Robert Hegner believes that three million is a conservative estimate. In his new book, *Parade of the Animal Kingdom*, Dr. Hegner says, "If we could emulate Noah and review a parade of the animal kingdom containing a pair of every species of animal known to science, and if these animals were to march by at the rate of one pair every three seconds, more than a month would elapse before the gorilla would make his appearance."

In order to use this great body of material it must be listed and catalogued. The present system of doing this is based on the work of the Swedish Naturalist, Linnaeus, who "attempted to express relationships found in nature and based his classification on similarities of structure." The first great biological division is into kingdoms, namely, the animal and plant kingdoms. The animal kingdom is then broken up into ten to twelve groups called phyla. Each phylum "is composed of a group of animals with a plan of construction common to themselves but which differs from that of the animals of all other phyla" (Arnold). Each phylum is further divided into class, order, family, genus, and species. The features which distinguish the larger groups are distinctive and easily recognized so in most books of zoology only the genus and species are given. The genus name is always capitalized while that of the species begins with a small letter. The species name is followed by the name of the person who first described the animal. For example, Cucumaria miniata (Brandt), Sea Gherkin. By this system an order is established which enables a student to find a particular animal and to know its general characteristics. This scheme of classification affords a method which is understood and followed by workers in all parts of the world. The Latin terminology is used because in pronunciation and form Latin is more generally understood than any other language. When there is a well-established common name, it is usually included with the scientific name, but too often the vernacular is strictly local in its use or the same common name is used for two or more different animals. Many of the less known animals, although of great importance to man, have no common names.

ANIMALS OF THE SEASHORE

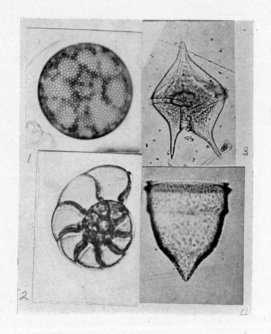

ONE-CELLED ANIMALS

Protozoa

1. Diatom—Coscinodiscus.
2. Protozoan—Foraminifer.
3. Protozoan—Peridinium.
4. Protozoan—Tintinnid.

All greatly magnified.

ONE-CELLED ANIMALS
Protozoa

PROTOZOA are one-celled animals and are so small that they cannot be studied without the aid of the microscope and special technique. Although invisible to the naked eye one-celled animals are extremely abundant in the water and are of utmost importance to the existence of more complex animals. In spite of the fact that a protozoan consists of a single cell it can carry on all the essential functions of higher animals—movement, nutrition, respiration, elimination of waste, and reproduction. One-celled plants are called diatoms.

The general term for the microscopic life in the water, both plant and animal, is plankton. The micro-plankton is composed of millions of one-celled plants and an equally large number of one-celled animals. Plankton in its broadest sense also includes the immature forms of more highly developed animals. Many animals feed upon the plankton and when one sees the tentacles of a tube worm or the appendages of a barnacle waving back and forth in the water the animal is engaged in securing plankton for its food. Most animals having siphons are dependent upon the plant and animal food suspended in the water. The luminescence seen in the water on summer nights is frequently due to the presence of certain protozoans which are capable of producing light .

It is impossible to estimate how many species of protozoans there are in the world but fifteen thousand have already been described. Protozoa cause many of our human diseases.

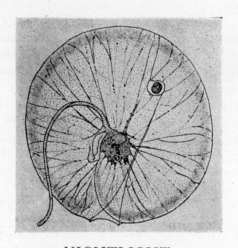

NIGHTLIGHT
Noctiluca scintillans

Greatly enlarged

NIGHTLIGHT
Noctiluca scintillans (Macartney)

DURING the summer months one occasionally notices a scum on the water which resembles tomato soup. This color is due to the presence of many *Noctiluca*, one-celled animals. "A gallon of such water contains as many *Noctiluca* as there are people in New York" (Hegner). At night when these tiny animals are irritated they give off a soft light which is produced without loss of energy to the animal. Sometimes as a boat sails through the water a path of light is left behind by these tiny creatures. Individually, *Noctiluca* are scarcely visible but millions of them massed together are conspicuous. A single specimen is about one twenty-fifth inch in diameter.

When seen under the microscope a *Noctiluca* resembles a crystal ball made of a delicate network of protoplasm. Two whip-like appendages, one thick, the other thin, extend from the mouth. The lightness of the liquid with which the cell is filled keeps the organism afloat. *Noctiluca* eat other animals smaller and weaker than themselves.

Like other protozoans, *Noctiluca* respond to external stimuli and changes of environment without the aid of a nervous system. Their usual mode of reproduction is by a division of the body into two nearly equal parts.

No group of animals is more interesting or important than the protozoans, but in this little study they must give place to their more highly developed heirs which can be plainly seen on the seashore.

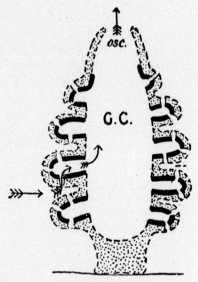

(Adapted from Hegner).

SPONGES
Porifera

Diagram of a simple sponge.
Arrows show course of water through
pores into gastric cavity (G.C.) and
to outside through osculum (OSC).

SPONGES
Porifera

THE group of animals known as sponges are the lowest of the many-celled animals. For a long time a heated dispute was waged concerning the position of sponges. Many scientists thought them to be animals and others believed them to be plants. Aristotle was the first scholar to decide with any certainty that they were animals, but their position was not definitely decided until the middle of the nineteenth century when with the aid of the microscope the matter was settled. After the sponges were established in the animal kingdom many students classified them as colonies of one-celled animals, but now the fact is accepted that they have cells of different kinds that perform functions similar to those of higher organisms.

Although sponges have a many-celled structure they stand near the bottom of the evolutionary ladder. They have no mouths, no stomachs nor any specialized organs. In fact, it is difficult to say just what constitutes a single sponge. If similar species come into contact with one another they may unite to form a single sponge, although sponges of different species will not thus fuse. A common method of propagating commercial sponges is to cut the living animal into pieces and if in favorable situaations the cuttings will grow into complete sponges. For these reasons and others, sponges are difficult to classify and identify.

Sponges, with the exception of one family, are all marine and are always stationary forms.

URN SPONGE
Grantia sp?

Slightly enlarged

URN SPONGE
Grantia sp?

GRANTIA is a small, graceful urn-shaped sponge that grows about an inch high and is of a grayish white color. It is a solitary form although clusters of them are frequently found growing on wharf piles, on stones, or in tide pools.

At the top of the sponge is a large opening surrounded by a circle of projecting spicules. The spicules are of carbonate of lime but the sponge itself is soft and slimy. The central cavity of the urn opens to the outside by a single large pore which carries off the water that has circulated through the body. Many small pores are present in the exterior wall of the sponge and through these water is drawn into the central cavity. Tiny animals and plants brought in with the water are engulfed as food material by the cells that line this cavity. The food is digested within the lining cells. The passage of water through the animal provides respiration through interchange of gases and also largely regulates excretion although wandering cells carry some waste to the outside.

The only movement of which sponges are capable is the opening and closing of the pores. Their only means of defense are their spiny spicules and unpleasant odor. These render them comparatively free from enemies although certain nudibranchs are known to feed upon them.

There are two thousand five hundred known species of sponges and they are world-wide in their distribution. Those found on the Pacific Coast are all small and of no value commercially. 9

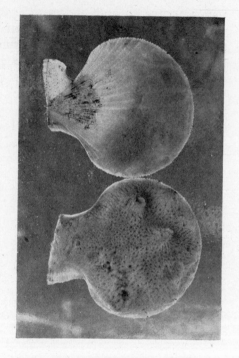

PECTEN SPONGES
Myxilla parasitica (lower)
Esperella adhaerens (upper)

Natural size

PECTEN SPONGES

Esperella adhaerens (Lambe)

Myxilla parasitica (Lambe)

NEARLY all the pecten, or scallop, shells in this region have the upper valves covered with a yellow or brown sponge. Two species are found on these shells in nearly equal quantities. The two differ considerably in their structure but to the casual observer they are quite similar. They are distinguished most readily by the size of the pores. Johnson and Snook say "In *Esperella adhaerens* the pores are very small and but slightly raised above the surface." In *Myxilla parasitica*, the incurrent pores are as large as the excurrent pores of the other species and the excurrent pores are much larger, having an average diameter of one-fourth inch. Both species are rather soft in texture.

The commercial sponge, as we know it, is only the skeleton of the animal. To the average person a living sponge would not be recognizable as the same animal as the commercial product. When alive the animal is a dark, unprepossessing mass filled with curious, microscopic, glassy spicules and the entire surface is covered with a slimy skin with many openings.

Sponges flourish best in warm shallow waters protected by reefs and islands where they attain a marketable size in one year.

Sponges have great varieties of shape, color, size, surface rigidity, canal systems, and types of surface. Some sponges are so small they are scarcely visible to the naked eye, while others are so large they are measured in feet.

11

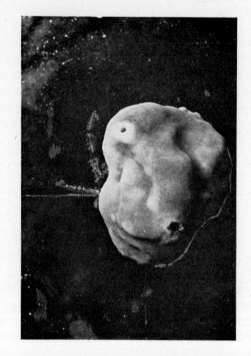

HERMIT SPONGE
Suberites latus

Natural size

HERMIT SPONGE
Suberites latus (Lambe)

THIS is an interesting sponge usually commensal with the hermit crab, but it may be found attached to rocks in deep water. The sponge, about two inches long and an inch wide, is an oblong compressed mass of fine, firm texture. Small inconspicuous openings of the pores give the sponge a smooth surface. Water is brought into the body through these small pores, while a few large excurrent pores carry it out.

Many of these sponges are pierced by a cavity in which a hermit crab lives. This relationship is brought about when a tiny sponge of this species settles upon a shell occupied by a hermit crab. Here it grows until the entire shell is covered with the sponge and by a process of absorption the shell is gradually disintegrated. The association of crab and sponge, no doubt, benefits both animals. The sponge secures transportation and the benefit of more food; the crab is protected by the drab looking sponge which few marine animals can eat. It also does away with the necessity of any change of shell, for the crab and the sponge grow up together.

Sponges, in general, reproduce by both asexual and sexual methods. By the asexual method a bud arises near the base of attachment; this later breaks off to form a new sponge; or the sponge may split in two equal parts by a process known as fission. Sexual reproduction takes place when eggs and sperm lying in the jelly-like mass of the body wall develop into larvae.

13

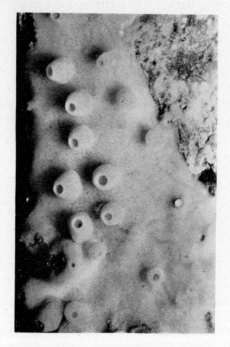

PURPLE ENCRUSTING SPONGE
Reniera rufescens

Natural size

PURPLE ENCRUSTING SPONGE
Reniera rufescens Lambe

THIS purple sponge spreads itself over rocks and stones at the water's edge. It forms an encrusting layer or carpet, irregular in shape and size. A mass sometimes measures a foot or more across. The body of the sponge consists of a network of cylindrical tubes varying in diameter from one-eighth to one-fourth inch which are fragile and easily pulverized. Arising from the main flat body are tubular processes about one-half inch in height with openings at the upper ends. The small openings bring in water bearing food and the large ones carry off the water. This sponge cannot be removed from its rocky base without being broken.

Three layers make up the body of the sponge. The dermal, or outer layer consists of flattened epithelial cells, the spicules of the skeleton, and the wandering cells; the gastral, or internal, layer is composed of muscular controlled collar-cells with flexible whiplike hairs that control the currents of water. The main mass of the body is composed of the middle layer having the functions of reproduction and framework. The framework of a sponge may be of a horny, silicious, or calcareous substance.

These inert animals are devoid of any nervous elements although, in some cases when an injury occurs within a centimeter of the excurrent pore, the stimulus will cause it to close.

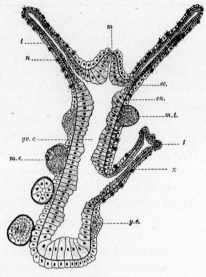

(Adapted from Hegner)

COELENTERATA
Coelenterata

Longitudinal diagram of *Hydra*.
ec. ectoderm; en. endoderm; gv.c.
stomach cavity; m. mouth; m.e. mature eggs; m.t. male organ; n. stinging cells; y.e. young egg; x. bud.

COELENTERATES
Coelenterata

SOME one has said that Shakespeare's description of old age, "Sans teeth, sans eyes, sans taste, sans everything," applies well to the coelenterates. They stand so low in the scale of development that the parts which perform the various functions show little differentiation.

Although the hydroids, jelly fish, sea anemones, and corals differ greatly in size, color, texture, and form, they are all alike structurally. The body of each radiates around a common center like the spokes of a wheel or the ribs of an umbrella. There is a central mouth which leads to a space serving for digestion and circulation. The central opening is surrounded with poisonous, stinging cells used to paralyze and capture the prey. Whatever enters the mouth circulates through the whole structure and when the food is assimilated the residue is expelled through the mouth.

The body wall consists of two cell layers, the ectoderm and the endoderm, with a jelly-like substance, the mesoglea, skeletal in its function, lying between. Many coelenterates are colonial in form and they may be either fixed or free swimming. Coelenterates reproduce by both sexual and asexual methods. In this group hydroids and jelly fish illustrate the phase of life history called alternation of generations. The offspring of these animals do not resemble the parents but are like the grandparents. The plant-like hydroids produce free swimming jelly fish which in turn deposit eggs and these develop into hydroids.

SEA PLUME
Obelia dichotoma

Natural size

SEA PLUME

Obelia dichotoma (Linnaeus)

THE sea plume is one of the most common and easily recognized hydroids of this region. It grows abundantly on wharf piling, rocks, seaweed, and floating timber. A basal stem gives off upright branches resembling those of a tree. These stems, which may be several inches long, are fine and thread-like and are of a gray or brown color. The branch ends in a hydra - like structure (hydranth) resembling the shape of a Greek vase. By means of a hand lens or microscope one sees the mouth in the center of the hydranth and arranged around its base there are about thirty tentacles. The tentacles act as a circle of guards to protect the animal and to capture food. Food material, ingested and digested by the hydra, consists of minute organisms in the plankton.

Like the hydranths, the reproductive organs arise from the main stem. The central axis of the reproductive organ is a blastostyle. The blastostyle gives rise to the medusa-buds which soon become detached and pass off as free swimming medusae, or jelly fish. The medusae in turn produce eggs which develop into hydroid colonies. William Beebe in his *Arcturus Adventure* says, "The actual transition from one generation to another, (is)— as astounding as it would be for a cat to have geraniums instead of kittens, and the plant offspring to scatter puppies in place of seeds." Dispersal of the species is brought about by the free swimming medusae. The soft parts of *Obelia* are protected by a chitinous covering which is ringed to allow for flexibility.   19

HYDROID

Abietinaria filicula

Greatly magnified

HYDROID
Abietinaria filicula (Ellis & Solander)

THIS hydroid is about two inches long and has alternating branches arranged on a slender stem; the branches may be divided more than once. The picture accompanying this sketch is highly magnified and shows the flask-like polyp cups of the feeding individuals growing close to the stem. Encircling the top of each polyp cup is a fringe of tentacles in the center of which is the mouth. The mouth leads into a stomach cavity which is in communication with the stalk and thus connected with the other members of the colony. The polyp cup serves as a protection for the tiny animal within. A delicate operculum made up of one to four parts covers the mouth of the cup when the polyp is contracted. Reproductive individuals, which are not shown in this picture, are larger than the feeding individuals. In this genus the reproductive individuals produce eggs and sperm without an intermediary free medusa stage.

Hydroids are small and inconspicuous and look more like plants than animals. They are very abundant on the shore attached to pilings and to rocks and shells where many of them appear as fuzzy, mossy growths. The smallest forms must be studied with a microscope and are so difficult to identify that only a specialist can hope to distinguish them. Ninety-eight species have been reported from the Puget Sound region but many of these occur in deep water.

OSTRICH PLUME HYDROID
Aglaophenia struthionides

Natural size

OSTRICH PLUME HYDROID
Aglaophenia struthionides (Murray)

THE ostrich plume hydroid has beautiful, delicate fronds which reach a height of six inches. From each side of the central stem regular, alternating branches arise. This plant-like growth is a colony of tiny animals in which the individual polyps are on only one side of the branches. The minute members of the colony are in cups sunk in the branches. In addition to the polyp cups there are much smaller cups which contain stinging cells. These are so small they can only be seen with the microscope. The entire colony has a protective transparent covering on the stems and it forms the cups into which the polyps can withdraw.

Some of the lateral branches of the colony have swollen flask-shaped structures which protect the reproductive polyps. In this hydroid free swimming jelly fish are not formed but egg cells develop into ciliated larvae within the reproductive individuals.

Dr. Nutting says that the plume hydroid has an effective method of capturing food. When a tiny plant or animal comes in contact with the stinging cells it becomes paralyzed. Then one of the adhesive pads on the defensive stinging polyps attaches itself to the prey and draws it firmly toward the tentacles and then into the mouth. The adhesive cells are cast off and remain attached to the victim.

THIMBLE JELLY FISH
Sarsia mirabilis

Three times natural size

THIMBLE JELLY FISH
Sarsia mirabilis L. Agassiz

THIS is a small, transparent, thimble-shaped medusa about one-half inch high and one-third inch wide. Four long, contractile tentacles, which may be four to six times the diameter of the bell, hang from the four radial canals. The manubrium, a stalk on which the mouth is borne, is long and slender and may hang far below the velum or may be coiled up within the bell. There is an eye spot on the outer side of each tentacle bulb and stinging cells are prominent near the ends of the tentacles.

The hydroid parent of this jelly fish grows to be three-fourths inch high and branches profusely. One cannot be sure of the hydroid forms of many jelly fish for unless the actual budding process is observed in the laboratory, the particular hydroid and jelly fish relationship is a difficult one to know. Both animals are so tiny and the sea so vast that observation of this process is highly improbable.

In spite of its delicacy and great beauty a jelly fish is a voracious feeder. It seizes its prey, which may be anything from plankton to small fish, with the tentacles. The tentacles are armed with stinging cells, each of which consists of a tiny sac filled with liquid and with a whip-like process coiled within. When the tentacles are touched the barbed stinging cells shoot out violently and penetrate the body of the prey. The victim is then pushed through the mouth into the stomach.

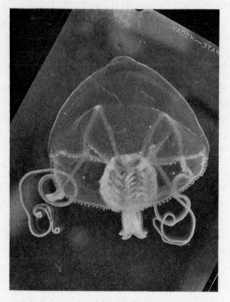

LONG MOUTH JELLY FISH
Stomotoca atra

Three times natural size

LONG MOUTH JELLY FISH
Stomotoca atra Agassiz

ANYONE with the slightest appreciation of rhythm responds to the graceful jelly fish as it moves leisurely through the water. An especially lovely one is this transparent, bell-like species which is approximately an inch wide and an inch high. Four radial lines divide the bell into equal parts and two long tentacles, which can be contracted or expanded, trail behind the animal when swimming. Eighty rudimentary tentacle bulbs are on the margin of the bell. Hanging below the center of the bell are the stomach and the four-lipped mouth. Eight to ten brown or white crossfolded gonads—reproductive organs—are on the sides of the stomach.

The hydroid stage of this jelly fish is probably a tubularian, a form which resembles matted seaweed. In jelly fish, eggs and sperm are produced in different animals. These reproductive cells break out into the water where fertilization takes place from the chance meeting of the two products. A ciliated larva develops from the egg. Then begins the most complex of life histories. The tiny larva settles down and becomes a hydroid instead of a jelly fish. At the unattached end of the hydroid a mouth appears, then four tentacles grow out around the mouth and the diminutive animal is able to feed. Other hydra-like individuals bud from the walls until a colony resembling the shape of a tree is formed. This type of development is called alternation of generations.

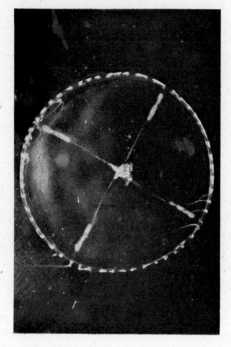

GREGARIOUS JELLY FISH
Phialidium gregarium

Three times natural size

GREGARIOUS JELLY FISH
Phialidium gregarium Agassiz

ANOTHER common species of jelly fish is the gregarious type. Seldom is a single specimen seen but great swarms of them travel together. The animal is rather small, varying in diameter from one-half to three-fourths inch and it is about half as high as it is wide. Four well defined radial canals divide the dorsal surface and near the base of the canals are thick white reproductive bodies. The mouth has four lobed lips and the stomach is small. Sixty tentacles, each arising from a spherical bulb, are suspended from the margin of the bell. In this jelly fish, as in most other forms, there are situated at the bases of the tentacles light recipient organs; between the bases of the tentacles are small sense organs known as lithocysts, or statocysts, which are probably organs of equilibrium and balance; there are also many cells sensitive to touch on the tentacles.

The hydroid form of this jelly fish is known to be about one mm. in height. It has an unbranched stem with a polyp cup at the top.

Another name for a jelly fish is a medusa. Medusa, as you remember, was a dragon-like woman in Greek mythology whose hair was a mass of writhing, twisting serpents. Many of our jelly fish have long, streaming tentacles that float out from their bodies as Medusa's hair did; and the little nettling cells in the tentacles sting somewhat as a serpent does.

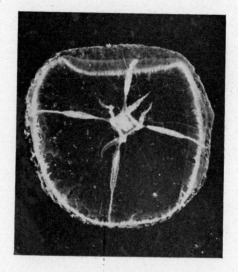

CROSS JELLY FISH
Halistaura cellularia

Natural size

CROSS JELLY FISH
Halistaura cellularia (A. Agassiz)

AN especially abundant jelly fish in Puget Sound is *Halistaura*. It measures approximately two inches in diameter and one-half inch in height and is entirely transparent. The cross jelly fish has four well marked radial canals which form a cross on the bell. Thick reproductive organs extend the entire length of the radial canals and from the edge of the bell hang one hundred to three hundred tentacles. When the tentacles are relaxed they may be two or three inches in length. The mouth and the stomach are clearly visible suspended on the under side of the bell. The animal feeds on minute organisms in the water captured by the stinging cells on the tentacles.

Jelly fish propel themselves through the water by the opening and closing of the bell. A jelly fish never rests and the rhythmic movement in the adult is continuous like the beating of a human heart. A jelly fish easily keeps afloat because its tissues are composed of ninety-five per cent water. This power of absorbing large quantities of liquid proportionately diminishes the weight of the jelly fish in the water until its specific gravity is nearly equal to the weight of the water. In jelly fish, the mesoglea, the jelly-like material lying between the two layers of cells, is extremely thick and gives the animal the jelly-like consistency. Jelly fish live only one season.

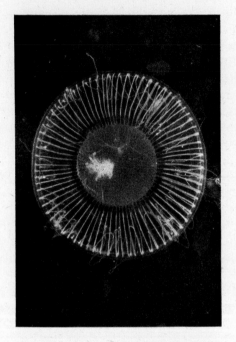

WATER JELLY FISH

Aequorea aequorea

Natural size

WATER JELLY FISH
Aequorea aequorea (Forsakali)

By for the most abundant jelly fish is *Aequorea*. The water near docks teems with these jelly fish swimming so near the surface they can easily be caught with the hand. A water jelly fish resembles a colorless circular piece of gelatine about two inches in diameter. It is three of four times as broad as it is high and it has from sixty to eighty radial canals extending from a central stomach to the margin of the bell. Reproductive glands are located on the radial canals. A large number of tentacles are suspended from the margin like a fringe. These tentacles serve in gathering food and can be coiled or lengthened to a considerable extent. A large ventral mouth opening, surrounded by minute lips, leads into the flat stomach. Food materials are carried through the body from the stomach by way of the radial canals. This jelly fish frequently eats other species of jelly fish and occasionally devours its own kind.

At night, the water jelly is highly luminescent, giving off a soft light. "Sometimes there are so many of these little light bearers traveling together that they make the waves look as if touched with fire." This luminescence shows at the bases of the tentacles and is probably due to the presence of certain enzymes or secretions. A water jelly fish often sticks to a boat oar at night where it looks like a circular ball of light. Many species of jelly fish are luminescent.

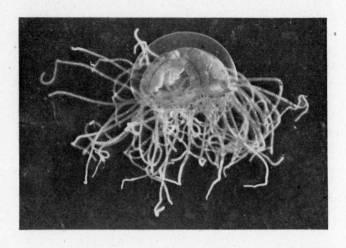

ORANGE STRIPED JELLY FISH

Gonionemus vertens

Two times natural size

ORANGE STRIPED JELLY FISH
Gonionemus vertens A. Agassiz

This brilliant species is found swimming among the eel grass and kelp along the shores. It measures about one-half inch in diameter and is somewhat higher than wide. The bell is yellow-green, the four radial canals are brown and the ribbon-like gonads on the radial canals are a deep orange-red. Sixty or seventy tentacles hang from the edge of the bell and each tentacle has a small adhesive pad near the outer end which allows the animal to attach itself to objects on the sea bottom.

The concave side of the bell is partially closed by a perforated membrane called the velum. Water is taken in through the central opening of the velum by the expansion of the body wall, and the contraction propels the jelly fish through the water. The mouth, which is on the under side, opens into a gastro-vascular cavity consisting of the stomach, the four radial canals and the circular canal. Food captured, while the animal is swimming, is conveyed to the mouth by the tentacles. Waste materials return by the same route and are discharged through the mouth.

The reproductive organs hang like a frill beneath the four radial canals. Striped jelly fish produce eggs and sperm which break out into the water where fertilization takes place. These fertilized eggs become fixed objects where they develop into hydroids. These in turn produce duplicates of their grandparents, jelly fish.

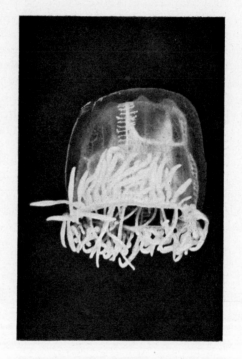

RED-EYE JELLY FISH
Polyorchis penicillata

Natural size

RED-EYE JELLY FISH
Polyorchis penicillata (Eschscholtz)

THIS jelly fish is a graceful, bell-shaped creature measuring one to two inches high and three-fourths to one and one-half inches broad. It inhabits shallow bays as well as the open waters. Its common name comes from the bright red eye spot at the base of each tentacle. There are from forty to one hundred and fifty tentacles arranged in two to four rows so the eye spots may be quite conspicuous. The tentacles are heavy and are placed close together around the margin of the bell. They are capable of considerable contraction and expansion; sometimes they appear as mere knobs and at other times trail behind the animal. Stinging cells on the tentacles capture food and provide defense.

A four-sided stomach hangs from a stalk in the center of the bell. At the end of the stalk is a mouth with four curled and fringed lips. On the lips are stinging cells which paralyze animals coming near them. Food is carried from the stomach into the four radial canals (digestive tract) from which arise thirty to thirty-two blindly ending branches. Six to eight gonads hang at the juncture of the radial canals and the stomach. The gonads are finger-like structures varying in length from one-fourth to two-thirds the depth of the bell.

Some red-eye jelly fish are nearly transparent while others have brown or purple stomachs, gonads and radial canals.

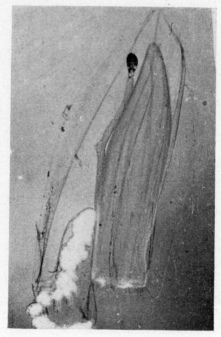

COLONIAL JELLY FISH
(Siphonophore)—Diphyes sp?

Twelve times natural size

COLONIAL JELLY FISH
(Siphonophore)—Diphyes sp?

DIPHYES is a beautiful, free swimming colony of minute jelly fish. The colony is arranged somewhat like a cluster of grapes attached to a common stem. The individuals that compose the colony vary according to their function and show a decided division of labor. Although apparently heterogeneously associated there is a common gastro-vascular cavity uniting the entire colony. "Some of the polyps are specialized for taking in food; some are armed with nettle cells, which protect the colony and help in capturing prey; some are swimming individuals, which propel the colony through the water; and others reproduce the species" (Johnson and Snook). In this species the swimming individuals are exceedingly large and the rest of the colony can be retracted into the groove of the swimming bodies. A colony consisting of thousands of individuals is buoyed up by a float. The most conspicuous feature of *Diphyes* is the large red eye spot at the front end of the colony. Small red bodies are numerous in the transparent body walls; these are probably drops of oil which partly sustain the colony.

Diphyes can expand or contract greatly, sometimes attaining a length of twelve inches. The colony is shortened constantly by the breaking off of the old terminal individuals. Each group that thus separates begins an independent life and becomes sexually mature.

This organism is only rarely found on the beach for it is a deep water form.

39

SAIL JELLY FISH
Velella lata

Two-thirds natural size

SAIL JELLY FISH
Velella lata Chamisso & Eysenhardt

OCCASIONALLY one sees a beautiful blue colonial jelly fish cast upon the shore. It looks like a tiny paper sail boat bobbing about on the water. There is a bright blue raft approximately three inches long with a triangular sail extending diagonally across the top. Usually these animals appear in schools and the waters off shore may be massed with them.

Sail jelly fish are fragile creatures which are tossed about by the winds and waves. The animal is kept afloat by air chambers in the raft and sail. If upset by strong winds the jelly fish soon dies for the little boat cannot reestablish its balance.

The individuals that make up the colony are attached to the under side of the float and hang down in the water. The individual polyps are hidden by the long tentacles which form a double row around the edge. A large feeding polyp is in the center of the colony and "between it and the tentacles are the reproductive individuals which also have mouths and are able to take in food, though they are much smaller than the central polyp" (Johnson and Snook). The polyps are all connected at their bases with the canal system which extends into the float and keel. The polyps and the tentacles bear stinging cells. Near the bases of the reproductive polyps are tiny jelly fish in all stages of development.

The Portuguese-man-of-war is a close relative of the sail jelly fish.

41

SEA BLUBBER
Cyanea capillata

One-fourth natural size

SEA BLUBBER
Cyanea capillata Eschscholtz

THIS is the largest jelly fish known. In some seas it reaches a diameter of seven feet but the Northwest variety is small, measuring from six to twelve inches. Its color is variable, ranging from orange to red with brown stomach and radial pouches. The umbrella of the sea blubber is nearly flat, shaped like a watch crystal. Eight deep clefts divide the margin of the umbrella and eight sense organs are situated in the clefts. Smaller, medium clefts appear in the margin between the large clefts and in these are also sense organs. Eight clusters of tentacles, each cluster having a hundred tentacle threads, extend from beneath the umbrella. It is said that the tentacles can lengthen many times the diameter of the umbrella. On the tentacles are stinging cells with which the animal combs the water in search of small fish, crustaceans, and other animals upon which it feeds. From the mouth hang four long, thin, folded mouth arms, the edges of which are ruffled like curtains. Great numbers of discharged eggs may adhere to the edges of the mouth arms. The gonads, egg and sperm sacs, lie in the four folded pouches near the stomach.

One writer records that certain small fish swim near the sea blubber and when danger approaches they all take refuge beneath the bell.

Irritation similar to that produced by nettles results from contact with the stinging cells of the sea blubber.

MOON JELLY FISH

Aurelia aurita

Two-thirds natural size

MOON JELLY FISH
Aurelia aurita (Linnaeus)

A MOON jelly fish is a large stinging form with a diameter of four to five inches. The flat disk-shaped body, made up of a tough gelatinous substance, is thick at the apex and thin at the margin. A fringe of short tentacles hangs from the disk. Eight definite lobes mark the margin of the jelly fish and a club-shaped sense organ is located in each marginal indentation. The central mouth, which leads into the stomach, branches into four long lips or arms, and free edges of which are notched and fluted and provided with small tentacles. Nettle cells cover the tentacles. From the four-lobed stomach the radial canals branch profusely until they join again in a circular canal just inside the margin.

Four horse-shoe-shaped gonads alternate with the mouth arms. Although the gonads are embedded in the jelly they are clearly visible on the dorsal surface. Gonads of the male are pink while those of the female are yellow. The gonads are connected with the stomach and discharge ova and sperm into the sea through the mouth.

Alternation of generations occurs in moon jellies but the hydroid stage is subordinate. The fertilized egg settles down and develops into a hydroid with a mouth, stomach, and sixteen tentacles, but soon the hydroid tube begins to show a series of disks shaped like saucers. In due course of time each disk develops tentacles and separates from those below when it swims away as a tiny jelly fish.

45

STALKED JELLY FISH
Haliclystus sanjuanensis

Natural size

STALKED JELLY FISH
Haliclystus sanjuanensis

THE stalked jelly fish is quite different in appearance from most of its relatives. Its umbrella is inverted with the part representing the spike attached to eel grass or other sea weed. It stands about an inch high and is the same width. The ribs at the margin of the umbrella are ornamented with eight clusters of short tentacles. Each cluster is composed of nearly a hundred tentacles borne on a short knob. Eight wide gonads extend from the apex of the umbrella to the cluster of tentacles on the margin. Situated on the margin between each cluster of tentacles is a large adhesive pad. This organ is shaped like a bean and is mounted on a short cylindrical base. The four-sided mouth is on the dorsal side in the center of the umbrella.

A stalked jelly fish can move about either by swimming or by crawling from place to place by means of its pads and adhesive basal stalk. This attractive animal is iridescent in color, transmitting various shades of green, yellow, orange or brown, which greatly enhance the beauty of the little creature.

Stalked jelly fish are found only in restricted areas.

The sea is full of animals that feed upon jelly fish. Most lower animals devour one another. If all the invertebrate animals produced were to live there would not be enough room for them in the sea.

SEA PEN OR SEA FEATHER
Ptilosarcus quadrangularis

One-fifth natural size

SEA PEN OR SEA FEATHER
Ptilosarcus quadrangularis Moroff

THIS strange colony of animals resembles a quill feather, hence the common name. A sea pen is structurally a type of coral that has a flexible, horny framework. The long, fleshy central stalk is naked below and is imbedded in sandy or muddy sea bottoms. A central axis of the stalk is of calcareous material to give it rigidity. The upper part of the stalk has two rows of opposite leaves. On the edge of each leaf are zooids, the individual members of the colony, which have mouth openings and body cavities connecting with the main canal which runs lengthwise through the colony. Minute tentacles around the mouth of each individual have stinging cells for defense and for gathering microscopic particles of food.

Sea pens are capable of great expansion, sometimes increasing from eight inches when contracted to eighteen inches when expanded. This expansion is brought about by taking in water through the mouths of the zooids and polyps or through an opening at the end of the stem. The stem of the sea pen is a bright orange color while the leaves are a lighter yellow edged with orange zooids. When the sea pen bends with the current of the water it looks like a beautiful plant. A sea pen is so unusual and striking in appearance that it will not be confused with any other animal. A sea pen lives in deep water, but occasionally one is washed onto the beach. At night the slightest touch will cause luminescence to spread from leaf to leaf until the whole is aglow.

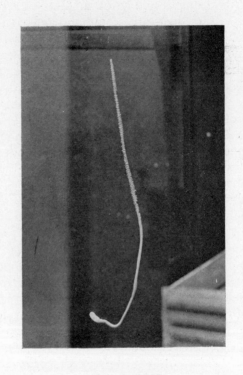

SEA WHIP
Stylatula elongata

One-fifth natural size

SEA WHIP
Stylatula elongata (Gabb)

A SEA whip is a strange gray or brown animal varying from one to three feet in length and one-fourth to one-half inch in width. It lives with the slender, lower end buried in the mud and the upper portion extending up into the water but it can move about slightly by changing the position of the base. Great numbers of minute individuals united upon a common stalk make up a sea whip. The lower portion is a bare stalk with a calcareous axis extending throughout the greater length of it to give the colony support. The upper part consists of small leaves arranged around the central stalk in a spiral manner and upon these leaves the individuals of the colony are borne. These tiny individuals, called zooids, carry on their own life processes but the body cavity of each is connected with the main stalk by a system of canals. There are two kinds of zooids, the nutritive individuals and those which convey water to and from the canals. There are about ten pairs of leaves to an inch with the nutritive zooids standing erect on the upper edges of the leaves. Each leaf is supported below by twelve to sixteen stiff, transparent thorns. The water-bearing zooids have neither tentacles nor ganads, and the mesenteries are undeveloped.

A sea whip has many characteristics in common with the corals and sea anemones and is a first cousin to the sea feathers. At least two species of sea whip occur in our waters.

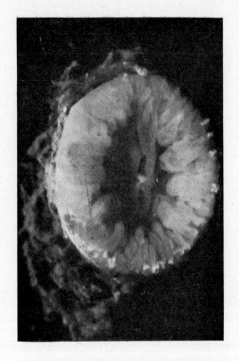

ORANGE-RED CORAL

Balanophyllia elegans

Four times natural size

ORANGE-RED CORAL
Balanophyllia elegans Verrill

ONLY one coral is found on the shores of the Northwest Pacific. The orange-red coral is a small solitary form, cup-like in shape with a bright, orange-red animal living within the limy outer wall. The cup measures from one-fourth to one-half inch wide and is one-half inch high.

A coral animal is really a tiny sea anemone that secrets a hard calcareous skeleton at its base and beneath the mesenteries. The skeleton is formed by the outer layer of cells and is external to the body. At the outer margin the cup is built up so that the animal can draw into it if it is disturbed. In a living animal there is a series of minute tentacles around the small mouth situated in the center of the disk. The disk is marked with lines which radiate from the center. A digestive tract connects with the mouth.

In tropical waters corals grow in large colonies, sometimes building up great reefs. Each member of the colony is a complete organism but is like every other individual of the group. Reproduction takes place either by sexual or asexual methods but the colony grows by budding—the type of budding determines the shape of the colony.

Coral reef animals do not live at a depth greater than two hundred or three hundred feet, yet coral reefs extend down thousands of feet. Their depth has been brought about by the gradual sinking of the reef and by a corresponding building up of successive layers of living colonies.

53

SUN ANEMONE
Metridium marginatum

One-third natural size

SUN ANEMONE
Metridium marginatum Ellis

SEA anemones are perhaps the most beautiful and striking of the seashore animals. The sun anemone, which resembles a huge brown or white chrysanthemum, is found growing abundantly upon the rocks and wharf piles near low tide mark. Beautiful orange and yellow forms are brought up from deep water.

A cluster of thread-like tentacles arranged like the petals of a flower stands upon a broad high column. The tentacle cluster may reach a diameter of six to eight inches. When the tentacles are touched they are immediately drawn into the column, making the anemone look old, wrinkled and shapeless. This transformation is like Cinderella, who at the stroke of twelve, lost all her finery. The change is brought about by contraction of muscle fibers and is a trick the anemone plays on its enemies to escape notice. One unfamiliar with its habits would scarcely recognize it as the same animal in the two aspects.

Like all anemones, the sun anemone is a cylindrical animal with a crown of hollow tentacles arranged around the central mouth. The tentacles are covered with numerous stinging cells which are used as means of offense and defense. Food consisting of small animals and plants captured by the tentacles is carried through a short gullet into the gastro-vascular (digestive) cavity. This is divided into many chambers by mesenteries. After the food has circulated through the chambers the undigested part is expelled through the mouth.

55

ROUGH ANEMONE
Cribrina xanthogrammica

One-half natural size

ROUGH ANEMONE
Cribrina xanthogrammica (Brandt)

THE rough anemones may be so numerous that they sometimes form a dense covering on the rocks in shallow water. Color in this anemone is variable for when exposed to sunlight it is green with purple or red on the ends of the tentacles. The green color is due to a small green alga in the walls of the column and tentacles. In the absence of sunlight the anemone is pale, delicately tinted with pink or lavender.

The disk of the anemone varies from one to three inches in diameter and stands upon a short column. The column may be contracted or extended so materially that the shape of the body is altered to a considerable degree. On the column are longitudinal lines and tubercles to which shells and other debris adhere. The thick, fleshy tentacles are arranged in six circles around the central mouth. These are equipped with nettle cells which are used in capturing prey. A gullet leads from the mouth into the stomach. The column which serves as a stomach cavity is divided into compartments by twenty-four partitions, called mesentries.

Ova and sperm are developed on the mesenteries and sometimes the products pass out of the mouth into the water. More often the young develop in the gastric cavity and later escape through the mouth of the parent as free swimming larvae but soon become attached and assume the adult character. It has been found that an anemone attains its full size when fourteen or fifteen months old.

57

SMALL GREEN ANEMONE
Epiactis prolifera

Two times natural size

SMALL GREEN ANEMONE
Epiactis prolifera Verrill

THE GREEN anemones often cover the bottoms of tide pools or attach themselves to eel grass, where they stand about one inch in diameter and three-fourths inch in height. The color is usually green but occasionally it is red or brown. Vertical lines of lighter color mark the short column and pedal disk. There are about ninety tentacles on a good sized specimen.

A most interesting feature of this anemone are the egg pits on the outside of the body. Specimens are frequently found with a row of tiny anemones all around the edge of the disk. They are like babies perched on the mother's back. The embryos in this case are retained within the body cavity of the parent until they have reached an advanced stage of development when they migrate to the pits where they attain the adult form.

The small green anemone is a voracious eater. If a tiny fish, a piece of mussel or a clam is placed on the tentacles, those touched by the food close over it and point toward the mouth. Cilia (hairs) at the mouth usually create an outward current of water, but when food is present they reverse their motion so that food is swept into the gullet. As soon as the food is safely in the stomach the cilia resume their outward beat.

Anemones are hardy creatures that will live almost indefinitely under favorable conditions. *Cambridge Natural History* reports that an anemone lived in an aquarium for sixty-six years and that many live for fifty years.

SEA WALNUT OR COMB JELLY
Pleurobrachia bachei

Three times natural size

SEA WALNUT OR COMB JELLY
Pleurobrachia bachei A. Agassiz

A GROUP of animals which to the casual observer resembles the jelly fish is the ctenophores or comb jellies. Like the jelly fish, they are transparent and gelatinous and move on the surface of the water, but they differ from them in structure, shape and method of locomotion. The body of the sea walnut is about three-fourths inch long, nearly spherical, and biradially symmetrical with a slit-like mouth at one end and a sense organ at the other. On the outside of the body are eight longitudinal ridges or combs that are covered with short, transverse rows of hairy plates arranged like the teeth of a comb. The movement of the cilia on the ridges of the plates propels the animal through the water. Sea walunts show a pink tint as prismatic colors play over the cilia.

Two long tentacles equipped with adhesive pads, used for capturing food, extend many times the length of the body. The tentacles are highly sensitive and contract quickly when they touch any object. They make long graceful curves as the animal moves slowly through the water. A funnel-shaped mouth leads into a gullet from which a complicated system of digestive canals develops. Eggs and sperm arise in the same animal and these escape into the mouth where they develop. There is no alternation of generations.

These delicate creatures are superlatively beautiful and are fascinating to watch. Large swarms of them often swim near the surface of the water.

TRANSLUCENT COMB JELLY
Beroe forskalii

Two times natural size

TRANSLUCENT COMB JELLY
Beroe forskalii Milne-Edwards

THE TRANSLUCENT comb jelly has an ovate, vase-shaped body one to two inches in length and three-fourths to one inch in width. On the upper rounded end is an eye spot and at the opposite end a very large mouth opens into a wide digestive tract. A complicated system of canals connects with the digestive organs. Most comb jellies are transparent but this species is decidedly translucent, having the appearance of ground glass. The general color of the animal is a delicate pink hue while the cilia are iridescent. Eight rows of ciliated plates extend three-fourths the length of the body and by their rapid movement the animal is propelled through the water in a nearly horizontal position. Its movements are slow and graceful. A translucent comb jelly has no tentacles.

This species is voracious and carnivorous, often feeding on other comb jellies nearly as large as itself. The translucent comb jelly usually appears alone but sometimes they are in great swarms. This delicate creature is so fragile that it is easily broken by rough water and storms. The translucent comb lives only one season for when the spawn is discharged its purpose in life is accomplished.

On occasions the sea contains thousands of jelly fish and comb jellies and at other times only a few will be seen. It may be that prevailing winds, tides, temperatures, or disturbances of the surface are contributing factors.

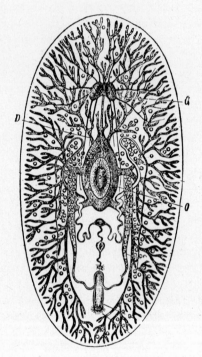

(Adapted from Hegner)

FLAT WORMS
Platyhelminthes

Diagram of a flatworm.
G. brain; O. mouth; D. intestine

FLAT WORMS AND NEMERTEANS
Platyhelminthes

To SOME people worms are repulsive creatures, unworthy of attention, but to many biologists worms are among the most interesting forms of invertebrate animal life.

The lower worms are divided, according to their shape, into two groups—flat worms, and ribbon worms—however, their internal structure is quite similar. Flat worms are broad, thin and leaf-like, while ribbon worms are long and narrow. Both flat worms and ribbon worms (nemerteans) are unsegmented, soft in texture, free swimming or parasitic, and usually sluggish in movement. All are flattened, being well adapted to living under stones and among sea weed. There is an anterior and posterior end but commonly no distinct head. These worms are carnivorous and take in food through the pharynx which is thrust out through the mouth to engulf the prey. Diatoms, larval mollusks, and crustaceans constitute their food. In flat worms waste is ejected through the mouth for the digestive canal ends blindly, but the ribbon worms have an anal opening.

Near the primitive eyes is a simple brain from which two lateral nerve cords lead to the posterior part of the body. Some worms move by a gliding motion due to minute hairs that cover the body, some glide by contraction of the muscular body wall, some species drag themselves along by attachment of the long proboscis and a few swim. The epidermis secretes mucous which leaves a trail of slime behind the animal.   65

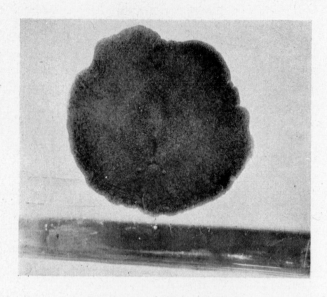

LARGE LEAF WORM

Cryptophallus magnus

Natural size

LARGE LEAF WORM
Cryptophallus magnus Freeman

A LEAF WORM adheres so tightly to the rock, is so thin and flat and is so nearly the color of the background that only a keen eye will detect it. The average size of this worm is from two to four inches in length with a maximum width of two inches and a thickness of one-eighth inch. A leaf worm varies in color with the environment but it will probably be tan interspersed with dark spots on the dorsal side and white on the ventral side.

When at rest the worm is broadly oval to circular in shape but in moving the length is slightly increased. The animal moves with a wave-like motion due to cilia that cover the surface but the margins of the body are folded and wrinkled by muscular contraction. The body is covered with a slimy secretion which helps the cilia to carry the body over all sorts of surfaces.

Two thick tentacles which can be extended one-fourth inch are on either side in front of the brain. There are about fifty minute eye spots which are sensitive to light but without sight on and around each tentacle. The mouth is on the ventral surface about half way between the anterior and posterior ends. This leads into a pharynx which is pushed out through the mouth when the worm is in search of food. The white internal organs which branch from the region above the pharynx can be seen through the lower surface. Waste material must be ejected through the mouth for there is no anal opening.

LITTLE LEAF WORM

Notoplana segnis

Three times natural size

LITTLE LEAF WORM
Notoplana segnis Freeman

THIS SPECIES of flat worm is extremely shy and elusive. It is plentiful in tide pools and under rocks at low tide where it adheres closely to the stones. Many tiny pigment spots may give the dorsal surface a gray or red-brown tinge but the ventral side is nearly white. A large specimen measures one inch in length and one-fourth to one-half inch in width and is so thin, it seems to be a mere film. A small leaf worm moves slowly by the cilia that cover the body. The cilia work in a mucous secretion given off by gland cells. The movement of the cilia often creates a slight disturbance in the water about the animal. A mouth is situated about midway between the ends on the ventral side and from it extends a digestive tract with many ramifying branches. The pharynx which is thrust out through the mouth in capturing food has a wide frilled margin. The pharynx presses against the prey and by the action of the salivary glands with which it is supplied the victim is softened and disintegrated. In this way the food material is partially dissolved before entering the digestive tract. Waste must be ejected through the mouth for the branched intestine ends blindly.

Eye spots, sensitive to light, are numerous on the dorsal surface near the anterior end. For the size of the animal the brain is large, having two rounded and symmetrical hemispheres.

Flat worms lay their eggs in flattened masses attached to rocks. The eggs hatch directly into tiny worms. 69

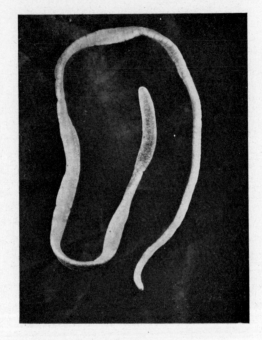

PURPLE RIBBON WORM

Emplectonema burgeri

One-half natural size

PURPLE RIBBON WORM
Emplectonema burgeri (Coe)

GREAT numbers of ribbon worms are sometimes
found under stones on sandy beaches where several may be coiled together in a complicated,
knotted mass. When this mass is unwound one sees
that each worm may be one to three feet long and
one-fourth to three-eighths inch wide. By muscular
contraction the worm is able to shorten the body
to a fraction of its original length. The color varies
considerably but it is frequently a mottled purple
or brown on the dorsal side and pale yellow or
cream color below. The skin secretes a vast amount
of slimy mucous which assists the animal in movement.

Like other nemertean worms, the purple ribbon
worm has a long thread-like organ, the proboscis,
which can be extended far in front of the body,
and is used as a feeler and an organ of offense and
defense. In proportion to the length of the body
the proboscis is short, scarcely more than one-tenth
the body length. The proboscis can be entirely
withdrawn into its sheath which lies above the digestive tract. Sixty or more minute eye spots are
situated on each side of the snout. There is no distinct head but near the anterior end the ventral
mouth opens into the pharynx. This leads into the
oesophagus which branches into numerous pouches
and eventually opens into the intestine by a narrow slit on the dorsal wall. Waste products are
discharged through the anus.

Ribbon worms have such a remarkable power of
regeneration that they can grow back lost parts
almost at will.   71

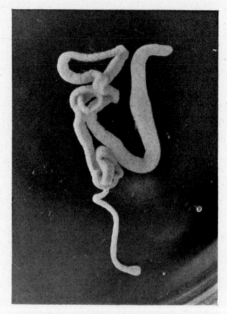

RED RIBBON WORM
Carinella rubra

About natural size

RED RIBBON WORM
Carinella rubra Griffin

THIS species of ribbon worm is distinguished by its soft, slender, rounded body and its bright vermilion or deep orange color. It is one of the most brilliantly colored worms known. Two feet is an average length for this worm but it is capable of such great extension and contraction that the length is hard to estimate. The width is about one-fifth inch at the head end, but the posterior end is much more slender. A broad band of dark brown, about two inches wide, reaching around the body, marks off the head from the body proper. The outside covering of the body is extremely thick and is filled with closely packed gland cells overlying circular and longitudinal muscle layers. The proboscis is about one-third the length of the body. This organ is attached by means of tissues around the mouth and is controlled by two large nerves. By means of the proboscis prey is pierced and at the same time it is held by the mucous secretion of the lining of the proboscis chamber. Central sense organs are highly developed.

A red ribbon worm is sluggish in movement and usually lies quietly under stones at low tide mark but it may be seen crawling on the sand in the water.

Some nemertean worms are hermaphroditic—male and female organs in the same animal—but more of them are unisexual. The reproductive organs lie along the intestine and open directly to the dorsal surface of the body.

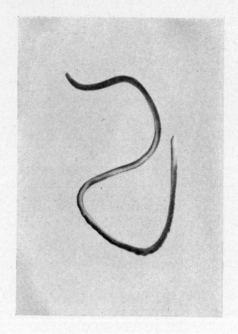

RESTLESS WORM

Paranemertes peregrina

One-third natural size

RESTLESS WORM
Paranemertes peregrina Coe

THIS worm receives its common name from its
habit of crawling about constantly on the sand or
stones on cloudy days. It is striking in appearance
with a dark brown or purple color on the dorsal
surface and white or yellow below. Some specimens grow to be eighteen inches long but six inches
is a more common size; the width does not exceed
one-fourth inch. The head end of the worm is
slightly flattened and the body is pointed at the
posterior end. A long proboscis, in connection with
the ventral mouth, is enclosed in a sheath above
the digestive tract. The proboscis is thrust out when
the worm is irritated or is in search of food. At
the tip of the proboscis is a braided stylet which
serves as a weapon of offense and defense. The
prey is pierced with the stylet and at the same
time is held by a mucous secretion from the proboscis. Several reserve stylets are ready for use if
one does not capture the prey. After the prey is
killed with the stylet the blood and other body
fluids that exude are devoured by the worm. The
worm is a voracious feeder, consuming numbers of
smaller worms and crustaceans.

The habitat of the restless worm is from low
water to high water mark in every variety of loca-
tion—on the sand, under stones, among sea weed,
and among barnacles. Its tenacity of life is remarkable.

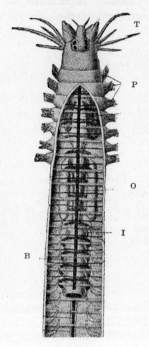

(Adapted from Hegner)

SEGMENTED WORMS

Annelida

Diagram of structure of clam-worm.
B. blood vessel; I. intestine; O. oesophagus; P. parapodia; T. tentacle.

SEGMENTED WORMS
Annelida

THE annelids are a group of worms which have elongated bodies composed of a series of ring-like segments and each segment has a set of similar and separate internal organs. There is a distinct head with a mouth, a well-developed brain and sensory organs in the anterior segment. The remaining segments are all similar and on these are bristles and other appendages. The alimentary canal, which extends the length of the worm, consists of a mouth, pharynx, oesophagus, intestine, and an anus. Red blood is transported through the body in tubes. Most marine annelids are unisexual but the reproductive organs are not well developed except in the breeding season. The eggs are cast out into the water where they are fertilized and soon develop into little free swimming larvae. In a few cases eggs and larvae are carried in brood pouches. Respiration is carried on through the body wall and in organs on the head or on the parapodia.

Some annelids live on plankton, a few feed on small animals, others eat seaweed and some burrowing forms digest the organic parts out of the material which passes through the body. A few annelids have plate-like scales on their bodies and live among rocks and hold-fasts of seaweed, and some live in tubes. Some tube dwellers make canals in the sand, others make tubes of mucous and seaweed, some have parchment-like tubes, and others build tubes of lime. Many annelids are highly colored.

77

SEA MOUSE

Aphrodita japonica

Two-thirds natural size

SEA MOUSE

Aphrodita japonica v. Marenzeller

THE sea mouse is an unmistakable form, not to be confused with any other. It closely resembles a mouse but it is really a segmented worm. Its body is broadly elliptical with a thick growth of bristles covering the entire back and sides of the animal. These bristles, about an inch long, project through a heavy felt-like covering which is the color and texture of a mouse's fur. (Who ever heard of a worm with a fur coat?)

A sea mouse lies buried in the mud below tide mark and the bristles are so covered with mud that it is difficult to distinguish the animal from its environment. When the sand and mud are removed the worm is highly iridescent and unusual. The body of this segmented worm is composed of fifteen pairs of modified scales but these are hidden on the dorsal side. The ventral side is bare, showing the segments plainly. From the edge of each segments project parapodia, leg-like appendages, ending in bundles of bristles. One pair of short tentacles and two pairs of long sense organs are on the head.

The average length of a sea mouse is three inches and the width is one and one-fourth to two inches at the broadest point, tapering toward each end. When handled a sea mouse rolls up until both ends meet. A sea mouse is not strictly a shore animal.

This strange animal was probably named in honor of Aphrodite, because she, too, was tossed upon the beach by the foaming breakers.   79

SCALE WORM
Halosydna insignis

Slightly enlarged

SCALE WORM
Halosydna insignis Baird

THIS worm has a series of eighteen, overlapping scales on the dorsal surface. The scales are a dark, mottled brown with a white spot near the center of each. The scale worm has a short, flattened body with almost parallel sides and bears on each segment two pairs of parapodia. This worm is approximately two and one-half inches long and one-fourth inch wide and is somewhat blunt at each end. Two tentacle-like structures extend beyond the head segment. The proboscis is large and has four powerful jaws at the end and a circle of papillae at the top.

Scale worms either are free living where they hide under stones, or are commensal (living with) in the tubes of other worms. Similar species may also be found on star fish, sea anemones, or on sea cucumbers. Individuals differ markedly in shape, color and size according to the conditions under which they live. Scale worms are sluggish in movement and when disturbed roll up until the two ends meet.

The scale worm readily throws off its scales when captured or kept in captivity. Observations have shown that this habit is deliberate and not the result of fragility. Only five days are required to regenerate a new scale and the original arrangement is achieved with remarkable precision.

The seashore is an interesting and stirring place to live but dangers due both to the elements and to other animals constantly beset the shore dweller.

LITTLE PILE WORM
Nereis procera

One and one-half times natural size

LITTLE PILE WORM
Nereis procera Ehlers

THIS common species of worm is from one and one-half to three inches long, somewhat rounded above and flat below, with a pair of parapodia on each segment. The fore part of the body is tinged with green but the posterior part is flesh colored. A pile worm lives in a transparent tube made of mucous which is secreted by pores in the body wall. When the animal is feeding it forces its body partly out of the tube. If the worm travels any distance it leaves the old tube behind and secretes a new one when reestablished.

A pile worm is fierce and voracious. It has a distinct head that is well equipped for attacking prey. The head consists of two parts: eyes, short tentacles, and sense organs, probably for testing food, form the fore part of the head, while four long tentacles used as feelers and the mouth make up the back part. The pile worm extrudes the pharynx, which is equipped with jaws for seizing prey, through its mouth. When the pharynx is drawn inside again it acts as a gizzard to tear the food into tiny bits. Excretory organs, ganglia of nerves, parts of the intestine and of the vascular system are in each segment except the head and tail. The tail segment has no parapodia but has a pair of long tactile feelers.

These worms swarm at night during the spawning season which coincides with the full moon of the summer months. During this time they frequently swim at the surface of the water.

CLAM OR SAND WORM
Nereis virens

One-half natural size

CLAM OR SAND WORM
Nereis virens Sars

A CLAM worm, the best known and most beautiful of the marine worms, has two hundred segments and may attain a length of eighteen inches
and a width of three-fourths inch, but specimens five or six inches long are more common. Male animals are a beautiful blue-green
color while the females are a dull green. In both
sexes the whole surface is highly iridescent, showing many brilliant hues. On each segment except
the head and tail, are parapodia ending in leaf-like
gills and bristles. The head is equipped with two
pairs of eyes, a pair of terminal tentacles, a pair of
thick sensory organs and four pairs of sensory
appendages. A well-developed proboscis ends in
pincer-like jaws. The digestive tract consists of a
mouth, a pharynx, an intestine, and an anus. Red
blood is contained in contractile blood vessels
which form a network of capillaries in the parapodia. The parapodia serve as organs of locomotion, as respiratory organs and as sensory organs.
There are circular and longitudinal muscles which
contract and expand the animal and also muscles
to move the parapodia.

Sand worms live in loose, flexible tubes of sand
and tiny stones held together and lined with a
mucous secretion.

The breeding season of clam worms seems to
coincide with the full moon of the summer months.
During this period the worms undergo marked
physiological changes, and swim about actively at
night.

SHELL BINDER WORM
Thelepus crispus

Natural size

SHELL BINDER WORM
Thelepus crispus Johnson

WORMS have such a variety of individual characteristics and specialized modes of living that they are a never-ending source of interest to a nature lover.

A shell binder worm may be found under stones, or on beaches of shale or boulders near low tide mark. It constructs a tube, a quarter of an inch in diameter, of sand and mud cemented together like a crude mosaic. Much foreign material clings to the tube to assist in making it inconspicuous. Mucous for cementing the materials is given off by thickened segments near the anterior end of the worm. Tubes can be made rapidly, as a new one is constructed after every journey into the world. The worm does not voluntarily leave the tube and only moves when disturbed or irritated.

Within the tube lives a worm four to six inches long with a body composed of sixty-three to ninety segments. The body is cylindrical, large near the head and tapering toward the posterior end. Three pairs of branched and plumed red gills and a semicircle of flesh colored tentacles, situated on the segment around the mouth, wave from the open end of the tube. The waving tentacles are coiled and may be extended many times the length of the worm. Prey is snared with the tentacles in the same manner that a cowboy throws a lasso.

As in other tube worms, the parapodia on the anterior segments of the shell binder are much reduced and there are no parapodia on the posterior segments.

87

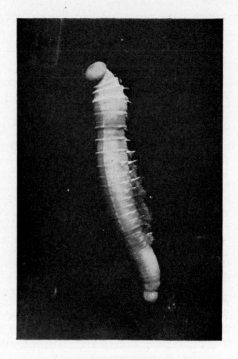

LUG WORM
Arenicola claperedii

Natural size

LUG WORM
Arenicola claperedii Levinson

FISHERMEN are familiar with the lug worm for it is frequently used as fish bait. A lug worm is brown-green, or almost black, in color and lives in a burrow in the sand from eighteen to twenty-four inches deep. The hiding place of the worm can be located by circular castings at the mouth of the burrow. Frequently it comes out of the burrow and crawls around on the sand.

A lug worm is cylindrical and averages six inches in length. The anterior part of the body, composed of six bristle-bearing segments, is much swollen and blunt at the end. No appendages appear on the head and the proboscis is unarmed. The posterior portion is without appendages but the slender, central part of the body has thirteen branching, red gills above the rudimentary parapodia. These bushy gills serve for respiratory purposes which, in view of their delicate nature and exposed position, seem ill suited to a burrowing animal. The undeveloped parapodia only serve slightly as organs of locomotion for a lug worm moves by wave-like muscular contractions of the body wall. An earthworm moves in the same manner. A lug worm is more or less sedentary and therefore has poorly developed locomotor organs, sense organs and breathing organs.

For food the lug worm swallows the sand through which it burrows. It assimilates the organic matter the sand contains and rejects the indigestible parts as castings. The life history of the lug worm is not completely known.

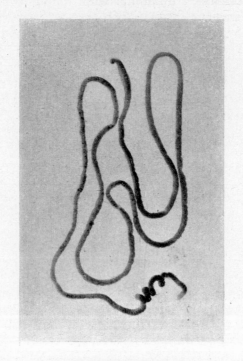

THREAD WORM
Lumbriconereis zonata

Natural size

THREAD WORM

Lumbriconereis zonata Johnson

THE thread worm is as slender as a fine cord and is from six to eighteen inches long. Almost every shovelful of sand dug from the beach will reveal several thread worms. The worm is so fragile that it is difficult to secure a whole specimen. The predominant color of the worm is brown, but each segment is marked with a darker brown zone which extends around the body.

A thread worm has a conical head without eyes or appendages and the mouth parts are perfectly smooth and glistening. Small parapodia ending in tiny tufts of bristles or sensory hairs are on each segment.

The habits of the thread worm are almost identical with those of the well-known earthworm. Like the earthworm, the thread worm burrows deep in the sand and does not make a tube. It is also a sand or mud eater. The earth and sand in which it burrows pass through the body where the food materials they may contain are digested and the inorganic parts pass off as waste matter. It has been said that through this process the mineral substances at the bottom of the sea have been modified as much as the soil of the land has been changed by the earthworm.

Animals that live in the sand and those that are fixed in habitat are usually without eyes, while forms that live on the surface of the beach and those that move about have organs of vision. To such an animal as a thread worm eyes would be useless and so nature has withheld them. 91

PLUME WORM

Eudistylia polymorpha

One-half natural size

PLUME WORM
Eudistylia polymorpha (Johnson)

THE plume worm lives in a translucent tube, half buried in the crevices of rocks and is so firmly attached that one needs a crowbar to pry out a whole specimen. The tube is made of a tough, horny material and may be encrusted with bits of sand or shell or small animals. Material for the tube is secreted by the body and the worm has been known to repair a broken tube.

The worm takes no chances with enemies, therefore, it never leaves the tube. Its only contact with the outside world is the projection of its head, surrounded by a circle of gills two inches in diameter, from the upper end of the tube. These gills look like a gaily colored red or green flower and are so sensitive that even the shadow of one's hand, passing over the tube, may cause the gills to retract. Each gill has from two to twenty conspicuous black eyespots. Food particles, extracted from the water, are swept into the mouth by the gills.

A plume worm measures from four to five inches in length and is approximately one-half inch wide, tapering to a sharp point or hook at the posterior end. Stiff bristles are on the thoracic segments and short setae appear on the abdominal segments. Muscle bands allow the animal to contract and expand.

Eudistylia gigantea is a similar worm that attains a length of eighteen inches. Clumps of sixty to one hundred tubes form groves in some localities.

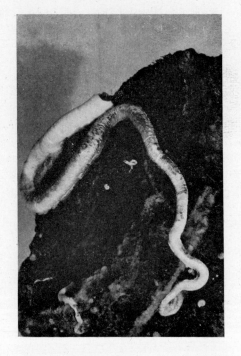

CALCAREOUS TUBE WORM

Serpula columbiana

Natural size

CALCAREOUS TUBE WORM

Serpula columbiana Johnson

A SERPULID worm differs from most worms by living in a white calcareous tube which it never leaves. Everyone has seen the tubes attached to rocks in tide pools or on stones near low water mark. The tubes are made by some mysterious chemical process in the worm's body by which the lime from the sea water is converted into the tube.

The worm that inhabits this tube measures two and one-half inches in length and one-fourth inch in width and is divided into about two hundred and fifty segments. Stages of growth in the worm are shown by circular ridges in the tube. A funnel-shaped operculum, or door, closes the opening of the tube when the worm draws within. When the fore part of the body protrudes from the end of the tube fifty-four branched, red gills, arranged in two spiral rows, wave in all directions. These moving plumes give the appearance of a delicate flower. Circulation of water induced by the cilia on the gills brings in oxygen and carries small food particles into the mouth.

There is also a small species of tube worm, *Spirorbis*, which builds its tiny coiled tube, one-fourth inch long and one-eighth inch wide, on seaweed or shells. The gills are feather-like and red and there is an operculum which closes the opening of the tube. The operculum serves as a brood pouch for the young. In *Spirorbis* the anterior abdominal segments are female and the posterior ones are male.

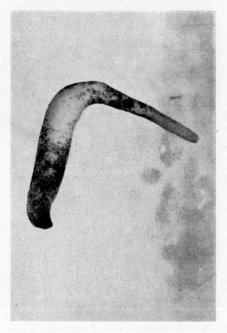

NAKED WORM

Sipunculus nudus

Natural size

NAKED WORM
Sipunculus nudus Linnaeus

THE naked worm is a cylindrical animal three to five inches in length. It is covered with a horny, white or flesh colored skin with dark, irregular patches of brown, and the body is marked off into small rectangular areas by underlying circular and longitudinal muscles. There are no parapodia or other means of locomotion, therefore, the animal moves by the contraction and expansion of the muscle bands. Very fine bristles, scarcely visible to the naked eye, cover the body.

The anterior part of the animal, to the extent of one-sixth of its length, can be introverted into the remainder of the body. In contracting, the introvert turns within itself until the entire region together with the sixteen tentacles disappears within the body of the animal. The rolling in and out of the introvert is kept up repeatedly by the worm. The introvert is smaller in diameter than the rest of the body and is controlled by many longitudinal muscle bundles and four retractor muscles.

At the posterior end of the body is a well defined anus. A coiled intestine extends the length of the body, as does a nerve cord from which are given off numerous smaller nerves. A rather complex blood vascular system is present in the naked worm.

A naked worm lives in sand or mud among the rocks but it makes no tube. Sand and gravel pass through the body as in the earthworm.

CORRUGATED WORM

Glycera rugosa

One-half natural size

CORRUGATED WORM
Glycera rugosa Johnson

THIS WORM is from ten to fifteen inches long and is made up of two hundred to three hundred segments. Its segments are well defined and of equal width, giving the worm a corrugated appearance; the animal tapers to a sharp point at each end. The corrugated worm is of a uniform, tawny, flesh color and lives in a cylindrical tube in the sand which it makes with its proboscis. All the parapodia are short and stout bearing simple, flat gills. The conical head is small and sharply pointed and on it are four minute tentacles and two rudimentary sense organs.

Of special interest is the long, club-shaped proboscis, or introvert, which is armed with four sharp teeth. With the aid of the proboscis and jaws the corrugated worm captures living animals for food. It probably acts as a scavenger by consuming quantities of decaying animal and vegetable matter. The enormous proboscis is protruded and retracted with astonishing rapidity and works in a manner similar to the finger of a glove being turned inward and outward. The hole left where the finger doubles in represents the mouth of the worm.

A corrugated worm burrows rapidly and disappears almost instantly into the sand or mud. The habit of burrowing in animals is particularly useful, not only in escaping observation of enemies but in avoiding the consequences of wave action and the retreat of the tides. This worm has the characteristic habit of coiling itself into a spiral when touched.

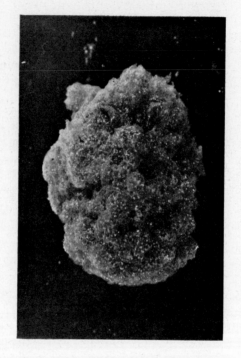

EGGS OF CORRUGATED WORM

Glycera rugosa?

Natural size

EGGS OF CORRUGATED WORM
Glycera rugosa?

FREQUENTLY a curious gelatinous mass about two or three inches across is found on the beach at low tide mark. This is, no doubt, the egg mass of the corrugated worm, *Glycera rugosa*, but the development has only been followed in the laboratory until the worm has twenty-five segments so one can not be sure of the parentage. It probably takes ten months or a year for the worm to reach maturity and it is difficult to keep the larva alive long under artificial conditions.

The egg mass is, in all probability, deposited by the mother worm during extreme low tide on a beach where there is gravel mixed with sand. When the mass is left on the sand it is a gray-green color but after several days it becomes brown due to the accumulation of diatoms (one-celled plants) on the surface. Enclosed within the gelatine are thousands of tiny eggs which begin to develop as soon as the mass is laid. After a week or ten days the minute worm begins to move in the egg. In due course of time the tiny creature, which now has a body composed of three or four segments, bursts the covering of the egg and crawls over the gelatinous mass. When it becomes larger and stronger the young worm swims about for a time in the great watery world. It then gives up its wandering and spends the rest of its life in a tube in the sand. By the time the worm reaches maturity it has two hundred to three hundred segments.

IRIDESCENT WORM

Hemipodia borealis

Natural size

IRIDESCENT WORM
Hemipodia borealis Johnson

IF ONE digs deep into the sandy beach a whole new realm of the animal world is revealed for the sand is as densely populated as is the surface. Worms are among the most numerous of the sand dwellers and they are of many kinds and of diverse habits. The iridescent worm is an attractive worm (if worms ever are attractive) of a clear flesh color which displays a beautiful iridescence near the bases of the parapodia. This worm is from three to six inches long and one-fourth inch wide, including the parapodia. It is of nearly uniform thickness for the greater part of the length, but tapers somewhat at the posterior end. There are one hundred and twenty-six segments in the body, each of which bears a pair of short parapodia composed of an upper and a lower set of bristles. The head is small, sharply pointed and bears four very short tentacles. When the pharynx is extruded it is about one-fourth inch long and is so stout that it appears too large for the worm. Four hook-like jaws are on the proboscis. With the proboscis the animal captures small worms and crustaceans for food.

This worm burrows rapidly and disappears almost instantly into the sand; as it descends it secretes a slimy mucous tube.

Worms are difficult animals to identify; even a worm expert rarely attempts to name a living specimen offhand. To be sure of species or even genera the use of the microscope and an examination of bristles and head appendages is necessary.

COLLARED TUBE WORM
Mesochaetopterus taylori

Incomplete worm and tube

Two-thirds natural size

COLLARED TUBE WORM
Mesochaetopterus taylori Potts

FROM THE middle of a sandy beach to the lowest tide mark, tubes about a quarter of an inch in diameter and an inch high project through the sand. The tubes are of a brown membranous material, covered with grains of sand and lined with a parchment-like substance. These tubes go straight down for nearly eighteen inches and end blindly. It is extremely difficult to obtain a whole tube or to procure a complete specimen of the worm.

The worm inhabiting the tube has a body divided into three distinct regions. The length of the entire worm is approximately fifteen inches and the width one-half inch at the broadest point. Seven segments measuring one inch form the anterior part of the worm; the median region has three broad segments measuring two and one-half inches; and the posterior region has sixty-eight segments measuring eleven inches. Parapodia are on each segment. The segments of the body are joined together by a narrow cord through which the intestine and the nerve cord run. This arrangement has the appearance of a string of beads. Generative organs in the posterior segments give them a rounded, swollen appearance.

The whole surface is a creamy white or yellow color with dashes of chocolate pigment on the mouth, the collar region and on the tentacles. In the posterior region the dark green intestine shows through the body wall. A very small mouth is at the anterior end but this is entirely hidden by a well-developed collar. Just below the collar two stout tentacles arise.

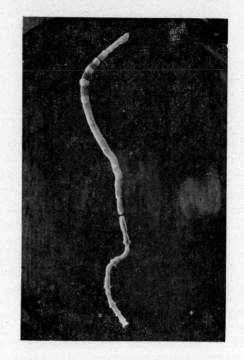

RED-BANDED TUBE WORM
Clymenella rubrocincta

One-half natural size

RED-BANDED TUBE WORM
Clymenella rubrocincta Johnson

WHEN walking on a sandy beach at low or medium tide mark a seashore naturalist is apt to notice hundreds of tiny brown tubes projecting about an inch above the sand. The tubes are made of coarse sand lined with a tough white membrane.

This tube is the home of an annelid worm but it is extremely difficult to see or procure the worm. The tube is about one-fourth inch wide and extends eight to ten inches down into the sand. Within the tube lives a slender worm one-sixth inch in diameter and seven inches long. In order to get a whole worm it is necessary to dig rapidly with a spade because the worm escapes at the bottom of the tube and breaks into many pieces. The tube also breaks easily.

If a worm is procured intact one will find that it is composed of twenty-two segments, being the widest at segments ten to twelve and narrowest at segments fifteen to seventeen. Around segments five to eight is a bright red band with a narrow white band in front. The last segment is funnel-shaped. There is a rosette of eighteen to thirty sensory appendages around the anus. The mouth has a thickened lower lip.

The worm does not leave the tube except from necessity. The worm projects the front part of its body from the tube and seizes for food the minute plants and animals suspended in the water.

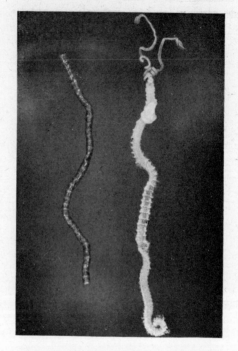

JOINTED-TUBE WORM

Telepsavis sp?

Natural size

JOINTED-TUBE WORM
Telepsavis sp?

WORMS have developed strange and diversified modes of life and are well adapted to their habitats. One species, the jointed-tube worm, has devised an underground tubular home made of translucent horny material. The tubes are so well hidden from the prying eyes of man that little is known of the private lives of this group of animals. It is extremely difficult to obtain a complete tube but if one digs carefully he finds that the tubes exceed a foot and a half in length, running vertically down through the sand and ending in a neatly rounded apex. The only evidence of the presence of the worm is a minute brown tube one-eighth inch in diameter extending an inch above the sand at low tide mark. The tube is jointed at short intervals and very fragile. A single individual measuring two inches in length and one-eighth inch in width occurs in each tube and from the end of the tube long tentacles project. The worm never leaves the tube except from necessity.

The worm is divided into two regions—the anterior, consisting of nine segments, and the posterior, consisting of thirty to forty similar segments. On the edge of each posterior segment is a bilobed parapodium bearing hairs. The ventral surface of the animal is tinged with a brown-purple pigment. The anterior part of the head which forms a collar bears eyes and two long tentacles.

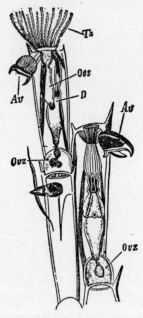

(Adapted from Hegner)

MOSS ANIMALS

Bryozoa

Diagram of a Bryozoan. Av. avicularium; D. digestive tract; Oes. oesophagus; Ovz. egg; Ta. tentacle.

MOSS ANIMALS
Bryozoa

THERE are nearly two thousand known species of Bryozoa and they are found in every ocean of the world from shallow water to the greatest depths, yet they are a group of animals not generally well known. They are small and inconspicuous and are often mistaken for seaweed, hydroids or corals. Frequently, these curious creatures encrust themselves in lace-like patterns on rocks and shells; hang from the blades of kelp; or grow in the crevices of the rocks like tiny trees. Fossils of bryozoans have been found from extremely ancient geological times.

Bryozoans form colonies consisting of hundreds of thousands of individuals that increase in size by a system of budding. New colonies arise from fertitlized eggs which develop into free swimming larvae. In some species the eggs are passed directly into the water but more frequently they develop in an embryo chamber. Later, the larvae settle down and give rise to new colonies. The colonies of bryozans may grow to be several inches high but the individuals of the colony are so small that they must be studied under the microscope to understand their structure.

Some colonies of bryozoans are rigid, some are flexible so they can be swayed with the tides, and still others are gelatinous and resemble the sponges. To distinguish species of bryozoans is a life-long task and the layman can only hope to recognize a few of the members of the group.

MOSS BRYOZOAN

Bugula pacifica

Eight times natural size

MOSS BRYOZOAN
Bugula pacifica Robertson

THE moss animal is a small plant-like bryozoan, one to two inches high, commonly found attached to rocks. The branches grow around a central stem in a spiral manner, forming dense clusters or erect tufts. The color of the moss animal is usually white but may be pale yellow, green or purple.

Individual members of the colony are called zooids and are so small that they cannot be seen without a microscope. When magnified they appear to be more or less cylindrical in shape with an outer wall of thick cuticle partially hardened by the presence of calcium carbonate. This hard covering, the zooecium, forms a case in which the soft parts of the animal lie. Soft parts of the zooid consist of the internal organs and the tentacle sheath. The mouth is in the center of the tentacle sheath and just outside of it is the anus. Below the tentacles the body wall is flexible and can be completely retracted within the outer covering. The body cavity is an extensive space lined with a single layer of cells and in it is a wide U-shaped digestive tract with the stomach at the lower end.

The moss animals have appendages near the tentacles called avicularia, which resemble birds' bills. These organs open and close constantly. The avicularia cannot convey their catch to the mouth so their function is probably not for capturing prey but to serve as defense organs and to keep the surface of the colony clean. The top of the zooecium may be closed by a flap-like door—the operculum.

STAG HORN BRYOZOAN
Bugula murrayana

Natural size

STAG HORN BRYOZOAN
Bugula murrayana (Johnstone)

THIS species of Bryozoa has flat, broad fronds and is found on rocky beaches where the waves beat hard. The branches, forked like the blunt branches of a stag horn, grow out from a main stem. A branch is approximately one-eighth inch in width and the colony may stand from one and one-half to three inches in height. One long root fibre or hold-fast may have dozens of stems, forming a bushy tuft, arising from it.

In this species the individuals of the colony may be clearly seen, each one appearing as a small perforation on the frond. From three to twelve rows of individuals occur on each frond. With the aid of a miscroscope one sees that each zooid has an avicularium, or bird's head appendage, and the outer cells have bristle-like tentacle filaments which constantly beat the wa'er to capture minute organisms upon which the animal feeds. The tentacles also function as organs of respiration and touch.

Both the male and female organs are located within the body cavity. The ripe eggs escape through the ruptured walls of the ovary into the body cavity where they meet the sperm cells. As a result of this fertilization the eggs develop into free, ciliated larvae. The larvae finally escape from the body cavity of the parent and after a time fasten themselves to suitable anchors and form the nucleus of a new colony which increases in size by a system of budding.

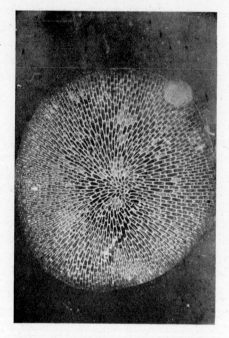

ENCRUSTING BRYOZOAN

Membranipora membranacea

Two times natural size

ENCRUSTING BRYOZOAN
Membranipora membranacea (Linnaeus)

ENCRUSTING bryozoans form thin, flat colonies, one or two inches in diameter, upon the floats and fronds of kelp and on rocks. One who is unfamiliar with this type of sea life would not think this irregular mold-like spot to be an animal. The encrustations are calcareous patches which are filled with small rectangular spaces marked off by narrow, white ridges. Within these spaces are the individual members of the colony which radiate out from the older, central part of the mass.

In order to understand the structure of a bryozoan it is necessary to watch it under a microscope. The microscope shows that the opening of each space is membranous and transparent with the individual animal within. The outer framework, the zooecium, has raised margins and a depressed front with a short, blunt spine at each anterior angle. Countless little tentacles, arranged in small funnels, move over the opening. With quick, jerky movements first one tentacle and then another turns inward and then the whole circle vanishes suddenly within the chamber below. One by one the tentacles appear again until the circle is complete and the mouth is seen in the center. Particles of food material in the water are drawn into the mouth by the hairs on the moving tentacles; the mouth communicates with a stomach and an intestine. There is neither heart nor vascular system but there is a simple nervous system consisting of a central ganglion and some strands of nervous tissue.

LACE CORAL BRYOZOAN

Retepora pacifica

Two times natural size

LACE CORAL BRYOZOAN
Retepora pacifica Robertson

THE "lace coral" is a beautiful little bryozoan. It is not a coral but resembles one because of the clear white color and the open meshes of the hard parts of the colony. This dainty species forms an encrusting base and from it a thin, perforated, semicircular lacy frill grows. These lace-like colonies grow to be an inch or an inch and a half high and nearly the same width and are attached to rocks or shells in the intertidal zone or in deeper water. Within each limy capsule of the lace lives an individual of the bryozoan colony. The colony increases in size by the system of budding.

This order of Bryozoa has great power of regeneration. At regular intervals the soft parts and internal organs of the animal break down and form a single brown mass called the "brown body." This "brown body" is expelled as waste matter and later new organs develop within the zooecium.

Being stationary animals, bryozoans have little need for sense organs and therefore they have degenerated and even the internal organs have become simplified.

The bryozoan must establish a secure footing on the shore where competition is not too keen, for it depends upon the currents of water to bring it sufficient food. It must also select a home where it is not left high and dry for hours by the receding tide. Most animals accustomed to obtaining oxygen from the water cannot change suddenly and use oxygen from the air.

SEA MAT BRYOZOAN

Flustra lichenoides

Natural size

SEA MAT BRYOZOAN
Flustra lichenoides Robertson

Rocks on the shallow sea bottom are often covered with luxurious growths of brown sea mats. In this species the bryozoan colonies grow erect with a number of broad, flexible branches attached by a narrow base. Each leaf-like branch may be one inch long and one-half inch wide. When observed through the microscope one sees that the hard, outer walls, the zooecia, in which the individual animals live, are arranged in two rows and in two layers and are more or less quadrangular in shape. These are rounded above with raised margins so that the tentacles and soft parts of the animals can be drawn within. The animal is further protected by a door and by spines on the outer edge of the zooecium. An avicularium extending above the zooecium opens and closes to keep foreign material from collecting on the animal. The tentacles lead into the mouth and there is a distinct digestive tube consisting of an oesophagus, a stomach and an intestine; the rest of the body cavity is filled with a colorless fluid. A sea mat has neither a heart nor a vascular system but white corpuscles are in the body fluid.

A noticeable fact on the seashore is that most animals are essentially flattened forms, for the need to reduce friction is apparent. This "stream line" is perhaps more evident in bryozoans than in any other group of animals for all of them are either flat, encrusting forms; or are flexible, bending with the direction of the current.

LAMP SHELL

Terebratalia transversa

Natural size

LAMP SHELL
Terebratalia transversa Sowerby

LAMP shells have a superficial resemblance to clams but a study of the shell and the internal structure shows them to be totally unrelated. Their position in the animal world is not entirely clear but in many respects they resemble the worms and bryozoans.

The lamp shell is common on most rocky beaches and is found from low water mark to a considerable depth. It is brown or white in color and may be one inch long, one and one-half inches wide and three-fourths inch high, but it is somewhat variable in shape. On the valves are numerous radiating ribs and concentric lines and the edges have several scallops, the central one of which dips downward. The dorsal (upper) valve extends beyond the ventral (lower) one in a beaklike manner; the ventral valve is smaller than the dorsal one and they are connected only by muscles. The shell is attached to a rock by a stalk that is stout and muscular. When the shell is open there can be seen within a pair of loops, called arms, which are respiratory and sensory in function and are also of use in the ingestion of food. Along one side of each loop is a row of ciliated tentacles and by these, minute organisms are swept into the mouth. The mouth lies between the arms and is without jaws or lips; it opens into a digestive tract made up of an oesophagus, a stomach and an intestine.

Lamp shells have come down from twenty-five million years of geological history. The genus, *Lingula,* is the oldest known genus of animals. 123

SNAKE'S HEAD LAMP SHELL
Terebratulina unguicula

Three times natural size

SNAKE'S HEAD LAMP SHELL
Terebratulina unguicula (Carpenter)

THIS is an attractive little shell, thin and transparent with a white or yellow cast. The shell is longer than it is wide, having a length of three-fourths inch and a width of one-half inch. Like all lamp shells, the lower valve has a perforated beak at the posterior end through which a stalk passes for attachment to solid objects. On the surface of the valves are numerous, delicate, radiating ribs which increase in number toward the margin of the shell. Lamp shells often grow in masses and seem to be able to move over one another by the stretching of the peduncle. Sometimes one may see the shell gaping open, displaying the strange tentacled arms or loops which lie coiled in the cavity. Minute living organisms alight on the tentacles and are engulfed as food.

The eggs are laid in the water where they develop into free swimming, ciliated larvae with a tuft of bristles at the head end. Soon the animal settles to the bottom and becomes attached by the posterior end. Two folds which are to secrete the shell then grow upward and enclose the body.

Lamp shells are not generally distributed over the earth but are localized, as is the case with many ancient groups of animals. The vitality manifested by these animals when kept in unnatural conditions is remarkable. This resistance probably accounts for their continuance, almost unchanged in character, through long geological ages.

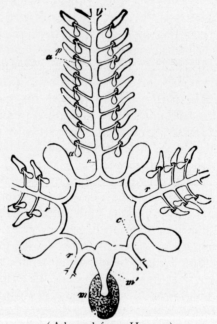

(Adapted from Hegner)

SPINY SKINNED ANIMALS
Echinodermata

Water vascular system of starfish.
m. madreporite; m'. stone canal; c.
circular canal; r. radial canal; p. tube
foot; a. suction bulb.

SPINY SKINNED ANIMALS
Echinodermata

THE phylum, Echinodermata, includes five distinct classes of brilliant marine animals: starfish, brittle stars, sea urchins, sea cucumbers, and sea lilies. Although quite different in appearance, all of these animals have the same general structure and many habits in common. With the exception of some of the cucumbers they are generally regarded in adult life as being radially symmetrical. Most echinoderms have bilateral symmetry—two equal sides—in the larval stages. All echinoderms have a water vascular system which controls the locomotor organs. Movement is effected by tube feet, bearing suckers, which can be attached or released by the action of the water vascular system. By means of the tube feet the animal drags itself along by a slow gliding motion. Besides the function of locomotion, the tube feet assist in the capturing of prey and are important tactile organs. Special sense organs are poorly developed.

Another common characteristic is the calcareous spicules or plates in the body wall which form an outer, spiny skeleton. Nervous systems differ in the classes but all have a superficial oral system consisting of a nerve ring around the mouth or oesophagus and five radial nerves which pass along the five radii. A distinct body cavity and a digestive tract are common to all. Sexes are separate in echinoderms. They have great regenerative powers. Nearly eight thousand species are known.

PURPLE OR OCHRE STAR

Pisaster ochraceus

One-fourth natural size

PURPLE OR OCHRE STAR
Pisaster ochraceus (Brandt)

THE shores are often lined with purple or ochre starfish at low tide mark or in shallow water. Purple and ochre specimens occur in equal numbers and there are many intermediary shadings.

A purple starfish has a thick, broad disk and five rather short, irregular rays, and measures eight to ten inches in diameter. A skeleton composed of a loose meshwork of calcareous plates gives the body a certain rigidity and protects the vital organs. On the aboral surface, spines of a light color form a distinct network on a dark background. Small pedicellaria, scissor-like spines, keep the body clean by grasping minute organisms or particles that may settle on the skin. Innumerable minute, transparent pouches project from the skeletal network and serve as gills, bringing about an interchange of gases.

A large elastic mouth is in the center of the disk on the under side. An ambulacral groove or furrow extends from the mouth along each ray and the tube feet arise from this furrow. A starfish may move at the rate of three inches a minute by means of the many tube feet. Tube feet are protected by a series of movable spines. The terminal tube feet of each arm have no sucking disks, but serve as feelers and olfactory organs and with these the animal gropes around. At the extreme end of each arm is an eyespot, sensitive to light but without vision. Believe it or not, the starfish has five eyes but cannot see.

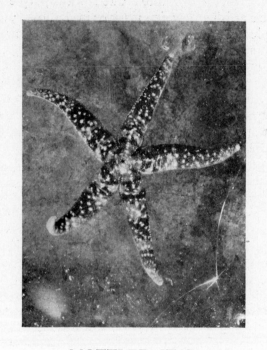

MOTTLED STAR

Evasterias troschelii

One-fourth natural size

MOTTLED STAR
Evasterias troschelii (Stimpson)

THE mottled starfish is common in shallow water or it is often exposed on rocks at low tide. It is a mottled brown-green in color with numerous thick spines arranged in irregular, transverse rows on the aboral surface. This starfish has five, long, tapering rays attached to a small, flat disk. The animal measures from eight to ten inches from tip to tip. Spines on the oral surface are short and are arranged in regular rows along the ambulacral grooves to protect the tube feet.

Water circulates through the body of a starfish by way of a water vascular system. Some one has called it a hydraulic locomotor system. Water enters the body through the madreporic filter, a sieve-like plate about one-fourth inch in diameter situated near the center on the aboral disk. It passes from the madreporic filter through a stone canal to a ring canal around the mouth and thence to radial canals which extend through each arm. From the radial canals small tubes connect with each tube foot. Reservoirs at the bases of the tube feet fill and withdraw the water like suction bulbs. By alternating the opening and closing of the suction valves the animal drags itself slowly along and moves with a gliding motion over all irregularities in the path of progress.

Hybrids are common among the mottled stars but there is, in general, little crossing between species of marine animals. Starfish breed in February and March in the Northwest.

131

SIX RAYED STAR

Leptasterias hexactis

Natural size

SIX RAYED STAR
Leptasterias hexactis (Stimpson)

THIS is a tiny starfish, rarely larger than two
and one-half or three inches over all. It is the only
genus in this region that regularly has six rays,
but two species are common. Six rayed stars are
often huddled together in dense clusters. In color
the aboral surface is a dull green blending into the
hue of the rock to which it adheres; the under side
is a pale yellow. The aboral spines are of equal
length and are arranged in five or seven somewhat
regular rows on each ray. Oral spines are long and
fine.

The sexes are separate in starfish. In most species eggs and sperm are thrown out into the water
in vast numbers and their coming together is a
matter of chance. The egg undergoes a typical development but the larval starfish is so unlike the
adult that for a long time it was thought to be an
entirely different animal. Most larvae are free
swimming but the six rayed star carries its eggs in
clusters in a pouch formed by arching the disk and
the young are retained in this pocket until they are
adult in shape and can take care of themselves.

The internal structure of a starfish is comparatively simple. A large folded stomach occupies the
greater part of the body cavity. A mouth and short
oesophagus lead to the stomach and a short intestine passes from the stomach to the aboral anus.
The nervous system has a central radial nerve ring
and radial nerve cords with nerve cells widely
scattered through the body.

LONG RAYED STAR

Orthasterias columbiana

One-fourth natural size

LONG RAYED STAR
Orthasterias columbiana Verrill

THIS starfish is best distinguished by the extremely narrow, humped disk and by the five long, slender, flexible rays. Specimens up to fifteen inches in diameter may be found. The long rayed star is most often a yellow color with irregular brown markings. On the aboral surface spines are arranged in five longitudinal rows with intermediary ones scattered between. These spines are long and column-like with wreaths of tiny spinelets on the top of each. Oral marginal spines are in two rows, those near the grooves being extremely fine.

Although starfish have a rather simple structure they carry on activities which require considerable coordination of parts. It would seem that the rigid structure of the starfish would make it difficult for the animal to turn over if it laid on its back. This, however, can be accomplished in a little less than a minute by the animal, turning a sort of handspring by means of its arms. "Professor Jennings taught individuals to use a certain arm in turning over. One animal was trained in eighteen days and after an interval of seven days 're-membered' which arm to use" (Johnson and Snook). This would indicate that starfish have a relatively high degree of intelligence.

Starfish are among the most beautiful and best known of all the seashore animals for they are found in all oceans and in deep and shallow water. Their unusual shape and brilliant colorings catch the attention of almost all visitors to the seashore.

SUNFLOWER OR TWENTY RAYED STAR

Pycnopodia helianthoides

One-tenth natural size

SUNFLOWER OR TWENTY RAYED STAR
Pycnopodia helianthoides (Brandt)

This is one of the largest starfish known, measuring from one and one-half to two and one-half feet in diameter and it is striking in color as well as in size. The Northwest form is ordinarily a beautiful mottled gray and salmon pink, but it may vary from orange to purple. The twenty or twenty-four rays make it an indisputable form. A study of the growth of a sunflower star shows that the young animal has but few rays, usually six and that new rays develop in pairs between the older ones. This species of starfish has a broad disk and the framework is much softer than in most stars; when picked up the arms hang limp and still. The arms radiate to slender points. Dense clusters of spines are on the thick soft skin of the dorsal surface.

One investigator (Verrill) estimated that there are forty thousand tube feet on a good sized sunflower star. Individually, the tube feet are not strong, but the combined power of forty thousand can be enormous. (Try to pull one off the rocks and see). The sunflower star is a voracious feeder, devouring many large clams and crustaceans daily.

Sunflower stars are numerous in shallow water but they are not often left exposed at low tide. This large starfish is only found in Pacific Coast waters.

Starfish were well known to Aristotle and to the medieval writers on animals. Nearly a thousand species have been described.

BLOOD STAR

Henricia leviuscula

One-half natural size

BLOOD STAR
Henricia leviuscula (Stimpson)

THIS starfish is brilliant red-orange or blood-red on the aboral side and a light yellow below. The disk is small and shallow and the five long, slender, rounded rays taper gradually. Its skeletal framework consists of so much lime that the starfish is quite stiff. Absence of long spines gives the animal a neat, well-groomed appearance. On the aboral surface can be seen minute spinelets with little spaces between, forming a fine network. The narrow oral grooves have only two rows of tube feet. The madreporic sieve plate, for the intake of water, is not well marked. Females carry their eggs in a pocket around the mouth.

This starfish varies in size from two to seven or eight inches in diameter; it ordinarily has five rays but four or six rays are not uncommon.

Starfish have a remarkable power of regeneration. Replacement of mutilated or entirely lost rays is a common ocurrence. A single ray with part of the disk has been known to grow a whole new animal. Injured arms may be deliberately cast off. Starfish have learned "in the course of time that it is better that one member should perish than that the whole life should be lost" (*The Haunts of Life*, Thomson). Many abnormalities are thus produced. To destroy undesirable starfish fishermen formerly cut them to pieces with the result that each part grew into a complete animal.

SUN STAR

Solaster stimpsoni

One-third natural size

SUN STAR
Solaster stimpsoni Verrill

THE sun star has a broad disk with eight or ten slender rays and measures up to eight inches from tip to tip. Markings are quite distinctive and are an almost certain guide in identification. A broad stripe of dull, blue-gray extends lengthwise to the tip of each ray and this is bordered on each side by a narrow pink stripe. The disk is also blue-gray. The lower surface is white with a gray stripe on each side of the ambulacral grooves. On the aboral surface are evenly grouped short blunt spines.

Starfish are carnivorous animals devouring large numbers of clams, oysters, and barnacles. A starfish has nothing in the way of teeth or jaws, but is able to open shells by devious methods. Shell fish may be taken into the stomach of the starfish whole and the shells are discarded later. But more frequently a starfish forces open the shell by fastening the tube feet upon it and exerting a steady pull until the muscle gives way and the shell opens. In doing this the starfish straddles the victim with the body humped up until only the tips of the rays are on the ground. Then a tug of war begins but the starfish always wins. Sometimes the stomach of the starfish is forced out through the mouth before engulfing the prey and within the stomach the plunder is slowly digested before entering the starfish's body.

ROSE STAR

Crossaster papposus

One-half natural size

ROSE STAR
Crossaster papposus (Linnaeus)

THE rose star is a beautiful member of the starfish family. This name is given to it because of its similarity to a rose, for it has two broad concentric bands of bright pink on a cream colored background, one on the disk and the other on the rays. It has a large flat disk with ten rather short rays and reaches a diameter of five inches. On the upper surface of the skeleton is an exceedingly rough, open network. This network is made up of tall, calcareous stalks bearing at their tips clusters of slender spines like minute brushes.

In the rose star the tip of each arm is modified as an optical organ which perceives distant light. There is, however, no evidence of image formation or detection of movement on the part of the eyes. Sense organs in starfish are scattered over the entire body but they are particularly numerous around the disks of the tube feet.

Starfish are highly destructive to all shell fish industries, especially to oyster beds. In one year starfish did $630,000 worth of damage to the oyster beds of Connecticut alone. Because of their remarkable power of regeneration they are difficult to kill, so oyster beds are now raked over with a tangle, an iron bar holding swabs of tangled rope. The spines of the starfish are caught in this device and many are gathered in each haul. They are then killed by steaming and the organic material used for fertilizer.

LEATHER STAR

Dermasterias imbricata

One-fourth natural size

LEATHER STAR
Dermasterias imbricata (Grube)

THE TERM leather star describes adequately this species of starfish. In a dried specimen the body covering resembles alligator skin. A living specimen is covered with a thick, soft, rough epidermis which gives off a mucous-like secretion. The disk is extremely broad and thick and is not well marked off from the five short rays. A conspicuous madreporic plate is near the center on the aboral surface. The tube feet are in narrow grooves and are protected by two rows of spines.

A leather star is a lead, blue-green color mottled with dull red, but like most species of starfish shows much variation in color. It is approximately ten inches in diameter.

When starfish are entirely exposed on the beach they are stranded and are waiting for the next tide to release them. These stragglers, slow moving at best, were intent upon their own occupations and so were left behind by the falling tide. Since they are now out of their natural element and cannot use their tube feet on a dry surface, they must remain inactive until the tide returns. Starfish living on wharf piling move up and down with the tide. When under water starfish move about quite freely. The exact technique by which a starfish walks is still a debated question. The tube feet may act as a rigid lever for pushing the body forward or may serve as a rope for hauling the animal forward.

BROAD-DISK STAR

Asterina (Patiria) miniata

One-third natural size

BROAD-DISK STAR
Asterina (Patiria) miniata (Brandt)

STARFISH are such colorful, lovely creatures that they are a never-ending source of interest to a nature lover. One handsome species is the broad-disc star with its brilliant color, broad disk, and short triangular rays. A good sized specimen measures six inches across and is commonly an orange color, varying to bright red or red-brown or purple, but it may be green or blotched with green.

It is thick in the center and thin at the margin, normally with five rays, but sometimes six. There are depressions on the disk between the rays. The entire dorsal surface is covered with spiny plates; the longer ones on the middle of the radial areas are crescent shaped. Between these are many small granulated, oblong and rounded plates; toward the margin they become rounded or elliptical. The spines on the under side are stout and blunt. Along the ambulacral groove is a comb of three to five rows of webbed spines. The madreporic plate, the dorsal sieve through which water enters the starfish's body, is conspicuous near the center of the disk.

The Northwest Pacific Coast seems to be headquarters for the shallow water starfish. No other region has anything like so many species, genera, families, or individuals. Starfish have evidently lived and flourished on this coast for many geological periods.

BRITTLE OR SERPENT STAR
Ophiopholis aculeata

Natural size

BRITTLE OR SERPENT STAR
Ophiopholis aculeata (Linnaeus)

THIS BRITTLE star lives on the rocky shores or on the hold-fasts of kelp. It has a disk one-half inch in diameter and rays one and one-half or two inches in length. The disk is gray mottled with white, while the rays are gray with brown bands extending across them; the oral surface is white. Conspicuous lobes are on the edge of the disk between the rays. Clusters of five spines occur on the plates along the edges of the rays.

The oral mouth is surrounded by five rigid projections called jaws and at the tip of each jaw is a plate bearing teeth. The jaws are not for mastication but serve as strainers to prevent the entrance of large particles of food into the mouth, for brittle stars eat only minute organisms lying in the mud. Food is scraped into the mouth with special tube feet, two pairs on each side. Most of the body cavity is occupied by the stomach which can not be extruded as in the starfish. The alimentary canal ends blindly, having neither intestine nor anus.

In general appearance, a brittle star or serpent star resembles a starfish, but on close examination is found to be quite distinctive. As the common name, serpent star, indicates, the animal has the writhing movement of a serpent, and the disk and arms are covered with plates or scales similar to those that cover a snake. The name, brittle star, comes from the fact that the arms readily break off when touched.

SMALL BRITTLE STAR
Ophiura lutkeni

One-half natural size

SMALL BRITTLE STAR
Ophiura lutkeni (Lyman)

THIS species of brittle star is shy and hard to find, but one can occasionally be seen under stones or on seaweed brought to shore from deep water. It is a small, delicate form with a five-sided disk one-fourth to three-fourths inch in diameter and the arms are one and one-half to two inches long. The ground color of the disk is gray, sometimes marked with black and white spots; the lower side is almost white. The disk is covered with several large, irregular plates surrounded by smaller ones, and the disk is notched over the base of each arm. Egg sacs lie between the arms and open by slits or pockets on the under side close to the rays. These pouches are believed to have also respiratory and excretory functions.

Like a star fish, a brittle star can regenerate new parts readily. It breaks off the arms voluntarily when injured and when it desires to escape its enemies. It is a matter of sacrificing a limb to save a life, "and what they surrender as a ransom for their lives they can regenerate at leisure" (*The Haunts of Life*, Thomson). The rapid movement of brittle stars is produced by wriggling and writhing with the arms.

The five rays of the brittle star are long and slender and are distinctly marked off from the small disk. Above and below the arms are covered with bare, calcareous plates and there are no ambulacral grooves.

BASKET STAR

Gorgonocephalus caryi

One-fourth natural size

BASKET STAR
Gorgonocephalus caryi Lyman

THE basket starfish is one of the most curious animals in the waters of the North Pacific. It is really a brittle starfish whose original five arms have branched and then branched again until there are hundreds of tiny branches waving and twisting in all directions. The ends of the branches are used for attaching the animal to seaweed and in capturing food. If a fish or other animal is caught in the tangle of writhing branches it hasn't a chance to escape. When capturing prey the branches form a basket similar to a fisherman's purse seine.

A basket star lives in rather deep water and is not strictly a seashore animal, but one is occasionally thrown upon the beach or may be caught on a fisherman's hook. The animal moves about by raising the disk high above the surface and then stretching the branches forward. The branches of the basket star are not as brittle nor as easily broken as are the arms of other brittle stars.

An average sized basket star measures from ten to twelve inches across and is covered with a soft yellow skin.

The mouth, on the under side of the animal, is made up of five "jaws". A number of tooth-like projections surround the mouth and serve as strainers to prevent large particles from entering the mouth. Most of the disk is filled with the stomach. There is neither intestine nor anus.

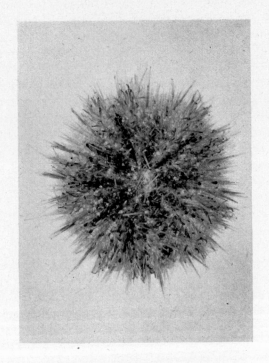

GREEN SEA URCHIN
Strongylocentrotus drobachiensis

About one-half natural size

GREEN SEA URCHIN
Strongylocentrotus drobachiensis (Muller)

THIS scientific name is perhaps the longest and hardest in scientific literature. (Learn it to amaze your friends). This difficult name refers in simple language to the extremely abundant bright, green sea urchin which resembles a chestnut burr. The animal is ordinarily about three inches in diameter, covered with spines one-half to three-fourths inch long. Perhaps, the sea urchin's prickly spines provide the most effective armour in the whole category of weapons possessed by shore animals.

Sometimes the rocks are completely covered with sea urchins at low tide mark.

Sea urchins are spiny, hemispherical shaped animals without arms. The skeleton of the sea urchin is composed of calcareous plates forming a case about the vital organs. The plates are made up of five hundred to six hundred pieces and are so expertly fitted together that on the external surface the seams are not visible. When empty, tests show the skeleton to be divided into ten divisions; five of these are narrow with small perforations, penetrated by tube feet, while the other five are wide, covered with great numbers of spherical knobs. Spines fit over these knobs like ball and socket joints. The movable spines together with the tube feet enable the animal to move in any direction. Scattered between the long spines are two types of smaller ones used for cleanliness and perception.

Sea urchins feed upon diatoms, seaweed, and small dead animals.

GIANT RED URCHIN
Strongylocentrotus franciscanus

One-fifth natural size

GIANT RED URCHIN
Strongylocentrotus franciscanus (A. Agassiz)

THIS is the largest sea urchin on the Pacific Coast. Giant red urchins may live in enormous colonies, literally covering the crevices of the rocks. Ordinarily the shell measures five inches in diameter and the thick spines are three inches long, making a span of nearly a foot. The animal is a red-purple color and is one of the most striking and interesting animals of the seashore. The muscular control exhibited in the movement of the long spines is amazing.

A sea urchin has many points in common with the starfish. A water-vascular system controls the spines and the 2000 tube feet. If the arms of the starfish are bent up until the points meet, the round ball would be comparable to the shell of the sea urchin. The alimentary canals of the two groups are similar. As in the starfish, the mouth is on the under side, but a sea urchin has a unique system of jaws. Aristotle, the Greek philosopher, who, by the way, was also a great naturalist, described the mouth parts and pointed out their resemblance to the shape of a Greek lantern. To this day the mouth parts are called Aristotle's lantern. The lantern of the red urchin is an inch or more in height. At the lower end are five chisel-like teeth attached to rough, bony plates that bulge in the center and meet again at the top. Lanterns from dead animals are frequently found on the beach and unless one is acquainted with them they are puzzling objects.

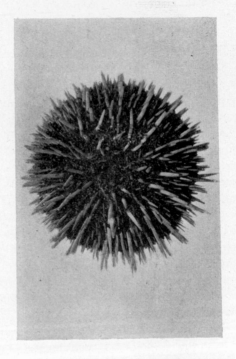

PURPLE URCHIN
Strongylocentrotus purpuratus

Two-thirds natural size

PURPLE URCHIN
Strongylocentrotus purpuratus (Stimpson)

A PURPLE sea urchin has a shell one and one-half to two and one-half inches across with thick blunt spines approximately an inch long. The spines do not stand straight up as they do in other species but lie in a somewhat horizontal position. Purple sea urchins are found in abundance on the rocks just below low tide mark.

Sea urchins pass their eggs into the water where they are fertilized. It is claimed that one female urchin will produce 20,000,000 eggs in one season. Of course, only a small portion of these develop, or are even fertilized. The sexes are separate and mature individuals have five large gonads in the upper part of the body cavity. Male sex products are white, while those of the female are a deep orange color. In many parts of the world the gonads are used for food. In France and the Orient they can be purchased in the markets and on many beaches they are eaten raw and unwashed. The natives insert a finger into the body cavity, bring out the gonads and devour the dainty morsel.

On exposed coasts some species of sea urchins drill holes into the rocks with their spines and sharp teeth. They force themselves within these holes to escape the beating of the surf. Frequently, they cannot get out and must spend the rest of their lives so imprisoned. In the quiet waters of Puget Sound none of the urchins burrow, partly because the granite rocks are too hard, and partly because they can find protection in crevices and tide pools.

159

SAND DOLLAR

Echinarachnius excentricus

Natural size

SAND DOLLAR

Echinarachnius excentricus Eschscholtz

A SAND dollar probably would not cause much stir in the financial market, but it is of value and interest to a seashore naturalist. It gets its name from the flat, nearly circular body, three inches in diameter. The disk is covered above and below with minute, velvety spines. Calcareous plates are fitted so closely together that they form a hard skeleton. In its natural habitat a sand dollar is an extremely dark purple-brown in color but when taken from the water it turns green and dead shells are white. Sand dollars are abundant in lagoons or on long, sandy beaches where they are half or completely buried in the sand. When only partly buried the upper surface slants in the direction the current is moving.

Etched on the dorsal surface, somewhat off center, is a delicate figure. This beautiful pattern, which looks like the petals of a flower, is for the protrusion of the respiratory tube feet. Sand dollars move by means of the tube feet and spines. All the spines move together in long, wavy lines like ripples on the water. The mouth is in the center on the under side and is provided with a flattened Aristotle's lantern. Sand dollars feed upon minute organic matter in the sand and water. From the mouth run ambulacral grooves which branch toward the outer edge. A sand dollar does not seem to be able to right itself if turned on the aboral side.

Fishermen make an indelible ink of the sand dollar.

BURROWING CUCUMBER

Leptosynapta inhaerens

Natural size

BURROWING CUCUMBER
Leptosynapta inhaerens (O. F. Muller)

THIS tiny cucumber burrows deep in the sand or mud and at first sight one might think it a worm. It lives in a tube made of fine grains of sand glued together with adhesive slime. A burrowing cucumber varies from one and one-fourth to four inches in length and is one-eighth to one-fourth inch in width. The mouth is at the anterior end of the body and is surrounded by twelve feathered tentacles. Five white lines extend the length of the body, marking the muscle bands, and the skin is covered with little white dots, the calcareous anchors.

The coiled intestine is nearly three times as long as the body. When the intestine of the animal is filled with food particles, the interior of the body appears as a dark, dense mass, but when the digestive tract is empty the burrowing cucumber is transparent and delicate. There are no tube feet or tubercles on the body wall, so the cucumber must depend upon the muscular contraction and expansion and the calcareous anchors to effect its movement. These microscopic anchors are held against the sand while the muscles contract from the posterior end, forcing the animal forward. The tentacles assist in movement by keeping constantly in motion, thus loosening and separating the grains of sand in the path of the animal's advance.

When kept in confinement this cucumber has a propensity to break itself into pieces by constriction of the body. Under favorable conditions the head can grow a new body.

163

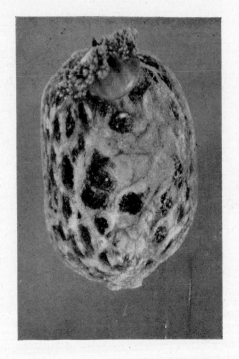

CREEPING PEDAL CUCUMBER

Psolus chitonoides

One and one-half times natural size

CREEPING PEDAL CUCUMBER
Psolus chitonoides Clark

As THE species name indicates, this creature resembles a chiton. In shape, it is quite different from the other cucumbers. The lower side is flattened to form a creeping sole. Tube feet appear in rows around the edge of the sole and extend lengthwise down the center of it. Large calcareous plates, irregular in shape, cover the plump dorsal surface. A long cylindrical neck near the front of the animal bears a profusely branched crown of crimson tentacles, which when extended are nearly as long as the body. The upper surface of the animal is a dull red color with lighter markings; the under side is flesh colored. This cucumber measures two inches in length and is approximately one inch wide. It hides itself under stones at low tide mark or in shallow water.

In spite of being uninviting and slimy to look at, certain cucumbers have longitudinal muscles inside the body wall that are very good to eat. In large species the muscle bands may be six to eight inches long. Some use of this source of food is being made commercially in the Puget Sound region. Sea cucumbers are used extensively for food in China and the South Seas, where they are partly sun dried and partly smoked and are sold in the markets as "trepang" or "beche-de-mer."

Respiration is brought about by the rhythmical contraction of the hollow, branched internal gills, where an exchange of gases takes place between the water and the blood contained in their walls.

RED SEA GHERKIN

Cucumaria miniata

One-half natural size

RED SEA GHERKIN
Cucumaria miniata (Brandt)

THIS IS a small red-brown cucumber, four to eight inches in length and one and one-half inches in diameter. It is found in large numbers under rocks or in crevices at low tide mark. Ten groups of densely branched tentacles surround the mouth at the anterior end. When the tentacles are extended they are continuously in motion and form a large, bright red rosette, but if the tentacles are contracted the animal loses its beauty and looks like a fat worm. Tube feet are situated along the five radii; those near the anterior end are considerably longer and darker in color than the posterior ones. Between the rows of tube feet the surface is comparatively smooth.

The sea gherkin is sluggish in movement but some progress can be made by the use of the tube feet and the contraction and expansion of the powerful longitudinal and transverse muscles that line the body wall. These muscles also allow the animal to change its shape in a remarkable manner.

Sea cucumbers have the curious habit of ejecting their internal organs when attacked or disturbed, but fortunately they can grow these organs again quite readily. This ejection takes place because the water in the body cavity is not compressible and when the animal is picked up or irritated it contracts and the water exerts a tremendous pressure on the body wall. As a result of this pressure the body wall tears near the anus and the whole of the intestine is pushed out.

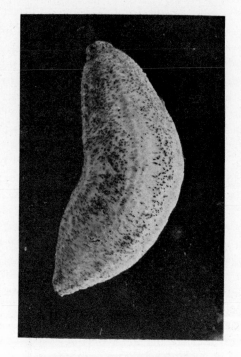

WHITE SEA GHERKIN

Cucumaria lubrica

Natural size

WHITE SEA GHERKIN
Cucumaria lubrica Clark

THIS SMALL white gherkin, about three inches long, lives under rocks at low tide mark. Many dark colored tube feet are arranged in two irregular rows along each of the radii. In sea cucumbers (gherkins) the radii are indistinct, longitudinal bands extending from the anterior to the posterior ends of the animal, but they serve the same purpose as the ambulacral grooves in the starfish. When in search of food, ten much-branched, yellow tentacles form a circle around the mouth, but when the tentacles and tube feet are retracted the cucumber looks like a fat worm.

When eating, the white gherkin licks its "fingers." Food particles contained in the sand and mud collect upon the moving tentacles, which are covered with slime. As there are no cilia (hairs) around the mouth to convey food to the opening, the tentacles must carry it there themselves. This is accomplished by turning the tentacles, one by one, toward the mouth and then pushing them inside, where the food is scraped off by a pair of Y-shaped jaws on each side of the mouth. The tentacles are then slowly withdrawn. In addition to gathering food, the tentacles are used as organs of touch and smell and they sometimes have ear sacs at the tips.

Some species of cucumbers have the habit of shooting out masses of sticky white threads which swell up in the water and confuse attacking animals.

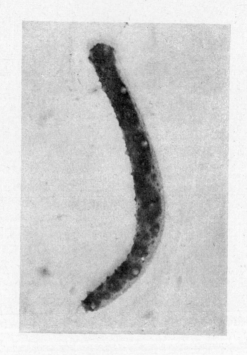

LARGE RED CUCUMBER

Stichopus californicus

One-fifth natural size

LARGE RED CUCUMBER
Stichopus californicus Stimpson

THE LARGE red cucumber commonly encountered along the beach reaches a length of fifteen inches and a diameter of approximately three inches. It is an elongated, cylindrical animal lying on one flattened side. There is a mouth at one end and an anus at the other. The calcareous plates in the body wall are minute and therefore the body is not rigid, but has a tough warty skin. Some individuals are a uniform red-brown in color while others are dark brown above and pale yellow below. Numerous large tube feet are arranged in rows on the under side and prominent conical projections are on the dorsal surface.

Fifteen tentacles around the mouth are borne on tall columns which end in rosettes of hundreds of tiny branches. When the tentacles are extended they twist and turn in all directions to catch the small organisms that come to rest upon them. A sea cucumber also eats organic material extracted from the sand and mud. The alimentary canal has a mouth, a pharynx, a short oesophagus, a small stomach, a long intestine which ends in a muscular enlargement called a cloaca, and an anus.

Water, which enters the cucumber's body through the internal madreporite and the anus, fills the respiratory trees or gills. A part of the water is forced into the body cavity, keeping the animal tensely dilated. Perhaps 50% of the body weight is the water in the body cavity. If the water is expelled the body is limp and slimy.

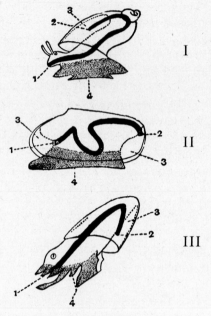

I

II

III

(Adapted from Hegner).

MOLLUSKS

Mollusca

Diagrams of types of mollusks.

I. Snail. II. Clam. III. Octopus
1. mouth; 2. anus; 3. mantle cavity;
4. foot.

MOLLUSKS
Mollusca

THE PHYLUM MOLLUSCA includes the chitons, limpets, slugs, clams, nudibranchs, snails, oysters, octopods, squids, and nautilii. More than sixty thousand species are known, and the great majority of these are marine. The mollusks' almost perfect preservation as fossils from the earliest periods of geological history has furnished the key to many problems of evolution.

It is difficult to give a concise difinition of a mollusk for although they have many characteristics in common the animals differ so greatly that it seems that nature resents attempts to circumscribe her living forms by definite rules. But we may say that a mollusk is a bilateral animal characterized by a soft unsegmented body. In most cases the body is protected by a shell, external or internal, but in some cases the shell is entirely wanting. When the shell is in one piece the animal is known as a univalve, when in two pieces it is a bivalve. In some forms the shell has eight plates. The shell is secreted by the mantle, an outer skin that more or less envelops the body. There is a muscular foot forming a flat creeping organ, a wedge shaped digging organ, or a modified structure forming long tentacle-like arms. A digestive tract, a circulatory system, and a nervous system are rather highly organized. In some mollusks there is a distinct head, but others are without heads.

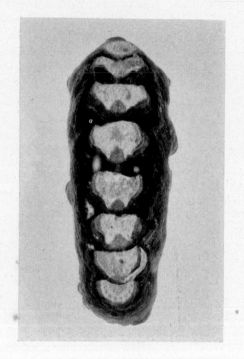

BLACK OR LEATHER CHITON

Katharina tunicata

Natural size

BLACK OR LEATHER CHITON
Katharina tunicata Wood

A LEATHER chitron can easily be distinguished by the eight calcareous plates of the dorsal shell. The plates are arranged longitudinally and overlap like the shingles on a roof. Along the outer edge the plates are covered by a girdle which is the exposed part of the mantle. The girdle is smooth, exceedingly tough, and very much thickened. In the black chitron the girdle nearly covers the plates, only about a third of each plate being exposed. The exposed parts of the plates are brown, sometimes with tiny barnacles adhering to them. If the girdle is removed one sees that the anterior plate has seven or eight slits or teeth and the posterior plate has one to four teeth.

Almost the whole of the ventral side of the animal is a foot with which it fastens itself securely to the rock, and upon which it creeps along. A large mouth can be seen clearly at one end just anterior to the foot and an anal opening is just behind the foot. The mantle completely covers the head; it has neither tentacles nor eyes. The foot and other soft parts are salmon colored. A black chitron may be three inches long and one and one-half inches across. When detached from its resting place it has the habit of rolling up in a ball and remaining so indefinitely.

The black chitrons are plentiful under rocks at low water mark and in shallow water. Chitrons are vegetarians and feed upon algae and diatoms.

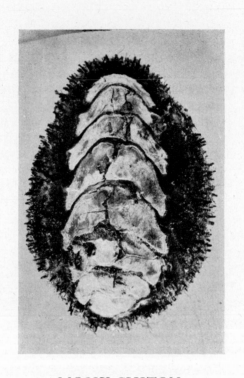

MOSSY CHITON

Mopalia muscosa

Slightly enlarged

MOSSY CHITON
Mopalia muscosa Gould

THE MOSSY chiton has a flattened, broadly ovate body with eight wide dorsal plates. The plates are much exposed and the surface is lusterless. Central areas of the plates have close, longitudinal ribs or markings. On the narrow girdle are many hairs which give the animal a mossy appearance. This species is usually a dull brown or gray color, although sometimes it is bright orange or a vivid green. An average sized specimen measures two and one-half inches in length and one and one-half inches in width.

A hinged effect in the plates is achieved by the posterior margin of one plate overlapping the anterior margin of the plate behind it. The loose spaces between the overlapping plates allow for the rolling up movement of the chiton.

In chitons the ventral mouth opens into a pharynx which has a long rasping organ, called a radula. This organ is provided with numerous teeth and with these the food is scraped off the rocks and torn into bits. The digestive tract is made up of a mouth, a pharynx, a short oesophagus, a stomach, an intestine six or seven times as long as the body, and an anus.

It is believed that many species of chitons are nocturnal in their habits and withdraw into shaded places at the approach of day. Sense organs are poorly developed in chitons.

Occasionally, detached plates of a chiton are picked up on the beach. Children call these plates butterfly shells or false teeth shells.   177

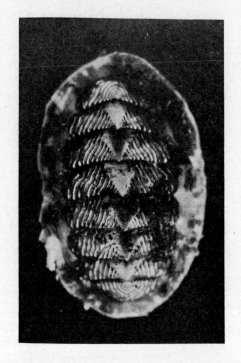

LINED CHITON

Lepidochitona lineata

Two times natural size

LINED CHITON
Lepidochitona lineata Wood

THE LINED chiton has a smooth, shiny surface moderately arched. In most specimens the ground color of the calcareous plates is a light buff or yellow marked with wavy, dark brown lines. Occasionally, the plates are unlined and are an even dark brown. The animal is approximately one and one-half inches long and nearly an inch wide. In order to keep the plates in place a smooth, thin girdle encircles the margin of the chiton. This delicate girdle allows a wide exposure of the plates. On the posterior plate are eight or ten teeth. Between the mantle and foot is a groove in which there are many pairs of gills.

The nervous system of chitons consists of a circum-oesophageal ring and two pairs of longitudinal nerve cords that motivate the foot and the mantle. The shell is pierced by minute, branching canals through which nerves reach the surface, where they terminate in sense organs, called shell eyes. The eyes appear as minute black spots which refract light. This is a primitive stage of nerve development. There is a heart with three chambers, one ventrical and two auricles, located near the posterior end of the chiton. The blood is supplied with oxygen in the gills. The internal structure of a chiton evidences a higher development than do the external features.

A chiton whose foot covers a square inch of surface can exert a pull of seventy pounds.

GIANT CHITON

Cryptochiton stelleri

One-half natural size

GIANT CHITON
Cryptochiton stelleri Middendorff

GIANT chitons are abundant near low tide mark. The brick red body covered with minute bright red tubercles is oblong, measures from six to eight inches in length and four inches across. The girdle is leathery and completely covers the eight dorsal plates. External plumed gills extend around the animal between the girdle and the foot. The large creeping foot attaches so firmly to a rock that a prying bar is necessary to remove the animal.

In chitons the sexes are separate but the females of the species deposit their eggs in various ways. Dr. Heath says that in one species, as soon as the male has liberated the sperm in a tide pool, the female begins to shoot eggs into the sperm. She discharges eggs at the rate of one to two per second for fifteen minutes, making a total of 1300 to 1500 eggs, which are about one-hundredth of an inch in diameter. In seven days a young chiton one-twentieth of an inch in length is hatched. Some species lay the eggs separately, each one enclosed in a chitinous envelope. In other species the eggs are in gelatinous strings attached to various objects. A few species retain the eggs in the mantle cavity while they undergo development and in one species the eggs develop in the oviduct of the mother. The eggs of all species hatch into free swimming larvae. After several weeks the animal settles to the bottom.

The chiton was highly esteemed as an article of food by the Indians.

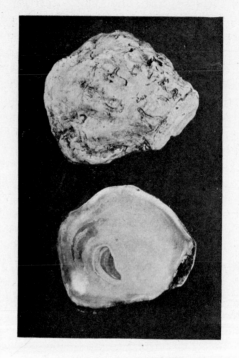

NATIVE OYSTER

Ostrea lurida

Two-thirds natural size

NATIVE OYSTER
Ostrea lurida Carpenter

OYSTERS native to the Pacific Coast are abundant but in many localities are too small to be of commercial value. The Olympia oyster is of marketable size and has a delicious flavor. The shell is rather thin but the surface may be made up of many irregular plates. The valves of the shell are of nearly equal size but may be either round or elongated. The lower valve, in which the oyster rests, is deep, while the upper one is slightly convex. An oyster shell of average size is two inches long, two and one-half inches wide and three-fourths inch in thickness. Native oysters are found in muddy bays where they are attached to stationary objects by the left valves.

"Methods employed by oyster farmers resemble those of agriculture, in that the bed is prepared, seed is sown, superfluous and foreign growths are weeded out, enemies are driven off, and the crop is harvested at certain seasons" (*Sea Beach at Ebb Tide*—Arnold). An oyster of medium size produces 16,000 eggs in one year. The larvae swim about freely for some time before finding resting places. Many are killed during the swimming period by changes of temperature and by enemies. Once settled, the young oysters lose the power of locomotion and become fixed. Oysters are thinned and replanted several times before they reach marketable size, which takes from three to five years.

JAPANESE OYSTER

Ostrea gigas

One-half natural size

JAPANESE OYSTER
Ostrea gigas Thunberg

NATIVE Olympia oysters could not meet the commercial demand for the product, so in 1905 seeds of Japanese oysters were imported and planted in Northwest waters. Their cultivation progressed slowly but in 1928-1929 it was given new impetus. At that time effective means of producing seeds at low cost were developed in Japan and since then hundreds of thousands of boxes of young Japanese oysters have been planted on the mud flats of the Northwest.

The waters of this region seem to be too cold to stimulate the natural spawning habits of the Japanese oysters so the seeds or spats are imported but in time the animals' habits will, no doubt, become adjusted to the temperature.

A female oyster may discharge half a million eggs in one season. The sperm of the male is given off into the water and the sex products come together by chance. When the eggs are fertilized they develop into free swimming larvae. After a short free swimming period the young oysters settle down on clean shells, rocks or other suitable materials on tide lands and there grow to maturity. Japanese oysters grow rapidly and may reach a length of eighteen inches and a width of several inches in three or four years. The shells are rough and often grow in clusters.

Oysters live on the microscopic plants and animals brought to them in the waters as the tides ebb and flow.

PINK PECTEN OR SCALLOP

Pecten hericius

Natural size

PINK PECTEN OR SCALLOP
Pecten hericius Gould

PECTEN shells with their rounded valves, wing-like ears and brilliant colorings are among the most beautiful objects found on the beach. An average sized specimen measures two inches in width, one and one-half inches in length, and one-half inch in thickness. In the pink pecten both valves have twenty-four fan-like, radiating, spiny ribs on a rose pink background, but the left valve is always darker in color than the right. On the upper valve the ribs are alternately large and small; on the lower valve the ribs are equal. The hinge margins are straight with unequal wing-like ears. Inside the shells are porcelain white with rose color near the fluted edges.

The internal structure of a pecten can be clearly seen. The mantle appears like a delicate frill all around the opening of the valve, and a row of tentacles hangs from the edge. Around the edge of the mantle are tiny eyes which shine brightly. Siphons are absent in a pecten, the mantle edges functioning for the incoming and outgoing water. The small foot is equipped with a byssal gland but the foot is not used for locomotion. When scallops are detached from the byssal threads they can swim about by clapping their shells together. The gills surround the abductor muscle and the large stomach lies beside it. Sex organs in the female are bright orange colored while those of the male are white.

SMOOTH PECTEN OR SCALLOP

Pecten hindsii

Four-fifths natural size

SMOOTH PECTEN OR SCALLOP
Pecten hindsii Carpenter

THE smooth pecten is only one and one-half inches in length and about the same in width. The right valve is almost white with twenty-six close-set, comparatively smooth, radiating ribs; the left valve is rose pink and the radiating ribs are only slightly spiny. Broad wing-like ears near the hinge are approximately half as long as the valves. In addition to the abductor muscle the valves are held together by a strong black ligament. The eyes of pectens are well developed and are not unlike those of higher animals.

Very frequently the beauty of our Northwest scallops is entirely hidden by a sponge that grows on the right valve. The sponge does not seem to injure the scallop and the sponge must be decidedly benefited by receiving transportation and access to increased food.

The artistic shape of the shells of pectens has been employed in conventional designs for centuries. Crusaders returning from the Holy Land fastened "St. James" shells on their garments and the design of the shell was adopted as the coat of arms of many knights in the Middle Ages. The "shell" in the insignia of the Shell Oil Company is that of a pecten or scallop.

Scallops are highly esteemed as an article of food in restaurants. Only the abductor muscle is usually served but other parts of the body are equally delicious. Scallops usually occur in beds below low tide mark and in order to secure them in quantities they must be dredged. 189

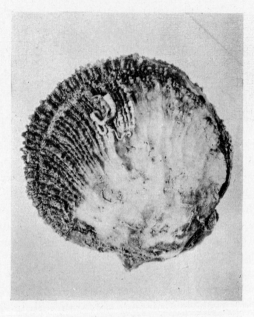

PURPLE HINGED OR ROCK SCALLOP

Hinnites giganteus

One-half natural size

PURPLE HINGED OR ROCK SCALLOP
Hinnites giganteus Gray

IN shape and general markings the rock scallop resembles the pecten, but its habits of adult life are different. When it is young the animal is free swimming and has a nearly symmetrical shell, but when it becomes three-fourths to one inch long it attaches itself to another shell or rock and settles down permanently. (Isn't this a human characteristic too?) When free swimming the young rock scallop is hard to distinguish from the pecten. If the object to which the scallop adheres is irregular the shell becomes more and more irregular. Nearly half the shell becomes so firmly attached to its rocky base that it is difficult to remove it without breaking. Tube worms, barnacles, hydroids, or other stationary animals fasten themselves to the shell so it is difficult to determine its real color.

The shell is thick and heavy and grows to be five to six inches in length and width. On the surface are many irregular, radiating ribs along which are rough, coarse spines. The hinge line is broad and heavy. There are no hinge teeth and the hinge ligament is embedded in a deep oblong pit. Inside, the shell is a clear, pearly white with dark purple markings near the hinge.

Bivalve shells are secreted by the mantle. The inner pearly layer is produced by the whole mantle while the middle and external layers are secreted only by the thick outer edge of the mantle.

ROCK OYSTER OR JINGLE

Pododesmus macroschisma

Natural size

ROCK OYSTER OR JINGLE
Pododesmus macroschisma Deshayes

THE rock oyster is firmly attached to a rock or shell by a short byssus which passes through a large hole in the lower valve. In this species the byssus is modified into a plate and serves to actually cement the abductor muscle to the rock. The valves of the shell are quite unequal. The lower one is deeply notched, small and nearly flat; the upper valve is circular and decidedly convex. On the upper valve are rude, indistinct ribs and here and there swollen and uneven knobs. The texture of the shell is delicate and is more or less pearly throughout with a predominance of green inside. It reaches a length of two inches and the width is approximately the same. There is no regular hinge but one side of the lower valve fits into a groove on the upper one. The gills are large and curved and all the organs are unusually placed on account of the byssal hole and muscle.

Rock oysters occur singly, rather than in great groups as do the commercial oysters and because of their rarity are not commonly eaten. Several Roman writers record the enjoyment derived by their fellows in the eating of oysters.

In sessile animals like the rock oyster the foot is unnecessary and so has become greatly reduced in size.

> "Slave to no sects, who takes no private road
> But looks through Nature up to Nature's God."
> —Pope.

EDIBLE MUSSEL

Mytilus edulis

Slightly enlarged

EDIBLE MUSSEL
Mytilus edulis Linnaeus

The edible mussels live in clusters fastened by a series of tough threads to pilings and rocks everywhere up and down the coast. Great numbers often grow upon one another in profusion. This mussel has a wedge shaped or triangular shell, rounded at one end, with the beak at the extreme opposite end. Conspicuous circular lines of growth are on the blue-black or olive colored shell. The height of the shell is nearly two and one-half inches and the length one inch. Inside, the shell is pearly white with purple margins. Hinge teeth are absent and the animal has only one siphon, the exhalant.

The foot is provided with a byssal gland that secretes the tough, fibrous threads. The mussel lifts its foot until it touches the gland and then draws it down to the rock or other solid base and between these two points a fine, brown thread is spun. This performance is repeated many times until there are a group of strands radiating outwards like guy ropes. The glandular secretion is like glue when secreted but hardens in the water. It becomes so strong and hard that violent storms cannot break the threads.

Mussels are comparatively stationary but by means of byssal threads they can move a short distance. The threads are thrown out in the direction the animal wishes to go and then by contraction of the muscle that controls the byssus the animal is drawn forward.

SEA MUSSEL
Mytilus californianus

Three-fourths natural size

SEA MUSSEL
Mytilus californianus Conrad

THE sea mussels like the pounding of the surf and are found in great beds along the open coast. They are frequently so numerous that they grow several layers deep, smothering and poisoning one another by the accumulation of waste products and silt that settle among them. This species of mussel is about four inches long and one and three-fourths inches high and has the same diameter as height. The beak of the shell is at the extreme anterior end and the shell is rounded behind. Somewhat irregular, circular rings and conspicuous radiating ribs mark the shell. Externally, the shell is black or dark brown and inside, it is white with violet markings. Mussels are always attached by the byssus in such a manner that the valves point downward.

Johnson and Snook report that the mussel deposits fully 100,000 eggs annually and it is known that the young animal grows from the egg to a length of three and one-half inches in a year. Most bivalves lay great numbers of eggs each year, a very small proportion of which hatch and still less ever reach maturity. Sometimes the whole body of a mussel, including the gills, mantle and foot, are completely filled with myriads of tiny, yellow eggs. The eggs hatch into free swimming larvae and these find shelter among the hold-fasts of seaweed. In due course of time a shell begins to develop and the tiny mussel is thrown upon the rocks by the spray. It then becomes attached by the byssal threads.

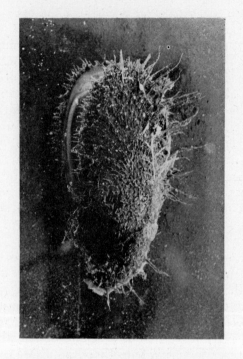

BEARDED OR HORSE MUSSEL

Modiolus modiolus

Two-thirds natural size

BEARDED OR HORSE MUSSEL
Modiolus modiolus Linnaeus

THE horse mussel is a solitary form which lives in rather deep water, but it is often washed upon the beaches attached to the hold-fasts of kelp. When in its natural habitat the horse mussel shelters itself in a nest constructed of marine refuse held together by the byssal threads. This mussel averages four inches in length, two inches in height and one and one-fourth inches in thickness. Its shell is much swollen, coarse, oblong and roughly wrinkled. A tough brown epidermis covers the shell and there are many coarse hairs near the ventral margin. A definite opening in the basal margin allows for the projection of the byssus. The beak is not directly at the end of the shell. The soft parts of the animal are edible.

Like all bivalves the horse mussel gets its food from the microscopic animals and plants in the water. Filmy portions of the mantle may project from the posterior end when the shell is open. Siphons in mussels are poorly developed, only the exhalant one being present. When there is not an inhalant siphon, food materials are taken in along the edges of the mantle. Unlike most mussels, this species is able to burrow, so it is sometimes found partially buried in the sand. The stationary habit of most mussels has resulted in the degeneration of the foot until in some species it amounts to no more than a tubercle.

COCKLE OR HEART CLAM

Cardium corbis

One-half natural size

COCKLE OR HEART CLAM
Cardium corbis Martyn

IF the shell of this clam is viewed from the side it resembles the shape of a heart, hence the common name. It has a large, thick, inflated shell with about thirty-seven close-set radiating lines with deep grooves between them. These ridges are marked horizontally with minute lines of growth. The ridges form deep indentations in the outer edge of the shell but near the beak the grooves are not so deep. Each valve has one prominent tooth near the hinge and one on each side at some distance from it. This clam is approximately two and one-half to three inches in length and height and two inches in diameter. A cockle is usually a yellow-brown, heavily mottled with darker brown spots; the beak is lighter in color and is nearly free of spots. Cockles are plentiful on sandy beaches, where they normally lie buried just beneath the sand between tide marks in sheltered areas.

This clam can move about easily with the aid of its muscular foot. The grooves in the shell help the foot to grip the sand. Cockles, like all clams, live on microscopic organisms in the water.

Age in clams may be judged by the annual rings on the shell which are similar to the annual rings in trees. Greater abundance of food and warmer waters cause the shell to grow faster in the summer and this difference is indicated by the narrow winter rings. Disturbance rings sometimes appear. Cockles have been known to grow one-fourteenth inch per week.

BUTTER OR WASHINGTON CLAM

Saxidomus giganteus

One-half natural size

BUTTER OR WASHINGTON CLAM

Saxidomus giganteus Deshayes

THE butter clams are exceedingly plentiful on our shores and are marketed in large quantities. A large butter clam may reach a length of four inches but those of three inches are more common. Shells of this species are solid, broad, and heavy, with rather poorly defined concentric lines of growth on the surface. The outside of the shell is sometimes yellow-brown, but the inside is always white. The two valves of the shell are nearly alike and are held together dorsally by a hinge ligament made of a tough, leathery substance. In the butter clam this ligament is mostly on the outside of the shell. In addition to the ligament the shells are held together by a system of four interlocking teeth which project from the hinge. Opening and closing of the shells is controlled by strong abductor muscles and by the ligament and cartilage of the hinge. When the valves are closed there is always a strain on the abductor muscles to overcome the resistance of the cartilage. When a clam dies and the pull on the muscles is relaxed, the valves gape open.

The umbo or beak of the shell is usually twisted or spiral and is the oldest part of the shell and the point at which growth begins. Calcareous secretions from the margin of the mantle are deposited upon the edges of the shell to increase the size. The lines of growth give the shell its circular ridges.

ROCK COCKLE OR LITTLE NECK CLAM

Paphia staminea

Two-thirds natural size

ROCK COCKLE OR LITTLE NECK CLAM
Paphia staminea Conrad

A LITTLE neck clam is easily recognized by the distinct lines radiating from the beak of the shell. These are crowded and numerous and are more prominent than the circular lines of growth. The circular and longitudinal lines give the shell a rough, checked appearance. This clam seldom grows to be more than three inches long; in proportion to the length it is high and rounded and is almost as wide as it is long. Color variation is from yellow to brown with brown angular spots. The margins of the shell are finely notched. Three hinge teeth are short and the ligament is thick and strong.

One of the most characteristic features of clams is the mantle. It is a thin, fleshy film of tissue which adheres to the inner side of each valve. The outer rim of the mantle is not attached to the shell and this free portion can be extended slightly beyond the margin when the valves are relaxed. In many clams the mantle edge is waved or fluted. Arnold says that, as the cover of a book envelops the printed pages, so the mantle entirely encloses the animal. Near the posterior end of the clam the marginal flaps of the mantle unite to form two openings or siphons which are used for the intake and expulsion of water. From the edges of the mantle come the calcareous deposits that form the shell.

The little neck clam is widespread and general along Northwest shores. This clam is sold in the markets.

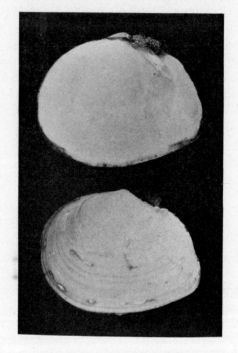

BENT NOSE CLAM

Macoma nasuta

Natural size

BENT NOSE CLAM
Macoma nasuta Conrad

THE bent nose clam has a delicate, flat shell which is rounded on the anterior margin, but is elongated and decidedly bent at the posterior edge. Two separate and slender siphons project from the bent end. A prominent external ligament and two teeth on one valve and one on the other constitute the shell hinge. An extremely thin, finely wrinkled, gray-brown skin covers the white shell, but the skin is sometimes partially worn off. The pallial sinus, the line of muscle attachment inside the valve, is distinct in an empty shell. A bent nose clam seldom grows to be more than two inches long and one and one-half inches wide. It inhabits muddy bays where it lives several inches below the surface.

Two pairs of flattened gills of mesh-like texture serve as breathing organs in clams. These lie in the cavity between the body and the mantle edge. The filaments of the gills are hollow and through these the blood circulates. Here the blood comes in close contact with the water, from which it takes up oxygen. The purified blood is then carried to the heart where it is pumped over the body. A heart with three well-developed chambers is present in clams. Waste products are thrown off through the gills and kidneys.

The bent nose clam is not extensively used for food at the present time but the kitchen middens of the Indians abound with them.

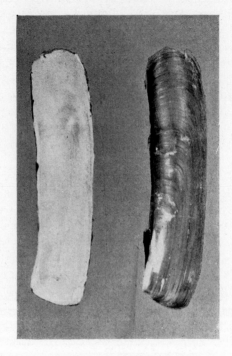

JACKNIFE CLAM

Solen sicarius

Natural size

JACKNIFE CLAM
Solen sicarius Gould

WHEN the foot and siphons of this clam are extended the shape resembles a jackknife with the blade open. The shell forms a slightly curved cylinder about four times as long as it is wide. To be more exact, the shell measures three inches in length, three-fourths inch in dameter and one-half inch in thickness. There is a small terminal beak and one hinge tooth in each valve. The anterior end of the shell is somewhat rounded but the posterior end is cut off squarely. The shell is open at both ends; from the lower end the foot protrudes and from the upper end the siphons project. A firm, glistening, brown skin covers the whole surface of the smooth shell.

Weymouth reports that the jackknife clam digs a smooth, lined burrow about fifteen or sixteen inches deep in which the clam lives permanently, moving up and down within it. The clam keeps in contact with the water by remaining about four inches down in the burrow and projecting the two siphons up through the mud. If the animal is disturbed, it descends quickly to the bottom of the burrow. The incomplete closing of the shell and the long protrusion of the foot and siphons would make the clam a choice tidbit for gulls and other predacious animals, so as a matter of safety it remains hidden in the burrow.

The jackknife clam, although resembling the razor clam in many respects, is not often used for food.

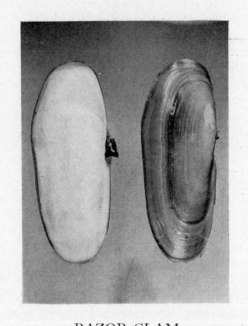

RAZOR CLAM

Siliqua patula

One-half natural size

RAZOR CLAM
Siliqua patula Dixon

THE razor clam is approximately five inches long and two inches wide. Its habitat is either on the broad, level sandy ocean beach or on one with a wide expanse of s'rong current. The shell of the razor clam is thin and fragile and is covered with a shiny, brown epidermis. A prominent umbo is situated about one-third of the distance from the anterior end and well-defined lines of growth extend from it. The anterior end of the shell is rounded, while the posterior end is somewhat blunt.

Razor clams burrow deeply in the sand and they have been known to bury themselves by eight or ten movements of the foot within seven seconds (Weymouth). The muscular foot, which is pointed in order to penetrate the sand readily, is extended half the length of the body. When the foot has been forced down as far as possible, it swells up until the diameter is greater than that of the shell. Then the foot contracts and the shell moves easily through the hole made by the foot. So firmly does the clam cling to the sand by the expanded foot that the shell may be pulled off the body before it will let go.

The razor clam is canned in large quantities in Washington. The living animal does not market well for the shell is so thin and closes so incompletely that it does not retain moisture long and therefore the clam spoils quickly.

HORSE CLAM

Schizothaerus nuttallii

One-third natural size

HORSE CLAM
Schizothaerus nuttallii Conrad

THIS is one of the largest clams found on our coasts. It may be four to six inches in length and it may weigh four pounds. The rather fragile shell is a dull white with poorly marked circular lines of growth. A thin, brown epidermis, falling in wrinkles over the margin, covers the shell. On dead shells the skin is absent. On the posterior end the shell is blunt and gapes widely, allowing for the projection of the large siphons. Even when retracted the siphons remain far outside the shell. The siphons are covered with a tough brown skin. On the anterior edge the shell gapes slightly for the protrusion of the foot. Teeth on the hinge are distinct; the beak is high and prominent. The presence of this clam can be detected on a sandy beach by small holes through which water shoots to a height of two or three feet. Most clams have this habit, but do not squirt water nearly so high. A horse clam is difficult to obtain for it burrows almost three feet into sand. The extremely large siphons reach to the surface and these can be closed by two valves of horny material. Small gray female crabs commonly live in pairs in the mantle cavity of the horse clam. They apparently neither help nor harm the clam. They are simply messmates.

Horse clams were used as food by the Indians but Americans consider them coarse. The Indians cooked the siphons (which are skinned before cooking) and all the soft parts.

MUD CLAM OR GAPER

Mya truncata

Natural size

MUD CLAM OR GAPER
Mya truncata Linnaeus

THE mud clam has a long shell measuring two and one-half inches in length, one and three-fourths inches in width and three-fourths inch in thickness. The posterior end is narrow, decidedly blunt and gapes broadly. Covering the whole surface of the shell is a brown papery epidermis which extends some distance beyond the margins. Long, united siphons protrude far outside the shell at the posterior end and a small foot projects at the other end. The siphons, which are covered with the paper-like epidermis, are so long they cannot be completely drawn into the shell. This clam is a burrowing form, inhabiting sand or mud. Mud clams have a special sac opening off the stomach which holds a reserve supply of food. Organic debris and small organisms in the water are swept into the mouth of the clam by the cilia on the gills and the labial palps.

In clams the posterior part of the mantle edge is modified into two well-developed siphons or tubes which control the incoming and outgoing currents of water. Through the lower siphon water flows into the mantle cavity, carrying with it microscopic food particles. By this same siphon pure water enters to bathe the gills. Through the upper siphon waste material and the water that has passed over the gills are ejected. In a few clams the siphons are poorly developed, being merely fusions of the mantle edges. This variation in siphon development is an adaptation of the habit of burrowing. 215

SOFT OR LONG CLAM

Mya arenaria

Two-thirds natural size

SOFT OR LONG CLAM
Mya arenaria Linnaeus

THE soft clam is not native to the West Coast, but is said to have been introduced with seed oysters about fifty years ago. It is now fully established and is as widely distributed as are our own forms. In California it is used extensively for food, but it is not generally marketed in the Northwest.

The soft clam has a delicate, elongated, smooth, white shell which is covered with a thin, gray-brown skin. Lines of growth are not clearly defined. The shell is somewhat flat and gapes broadly, and the beak is central and bends backwards. At the posterior end the valve is flatter and more elongated than the anterior end to allow for the extrusion of the long, stout siphons which cannot be entirely drawn into the shell. Teeth are not well developed on the valves, but a prominent shelf-like process protrudes near the hinge, and the ligament is strong.

The soft clam is fairly constant in size and shape, being nearly two and one-half inches long, one and one-half inches high and three-fourths inch thick. This clam's presence is indicated at low tide by a small hole in the sand through which water squirts occasionally. During high tide its siphons project through this hole.

Irregular lines and markings on the inside of dead clam shells show where the abductor muscles and the mantle were attached.

> "Go forth under the open sky and list
> to nature's teachings."—Bryant.

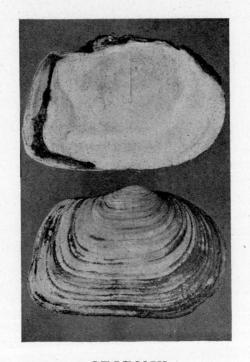

GEODUCK

Panope generosa

One-third natural size

GEODUCK
Panope generosa Gould

THE geoduck is the largest burrowing clam in this region. It has a shell which reaches a length of six inches and the animal may weigh six pounds. The shell is large, heavy, a chalky white and is marked with coarse, circular lines of growth. A dirty, yellow, wrinkled skin covers the whole surface of the shell. The shell is almost square, the basal and hinge margins being nearly parallel. A narrow hinge with one erect triangular tooth and an external ligament, together with the abductor muscles, control the opening and the closing of the shell. On the blunt posterior margin the shell gapes broadly to allow for the projection of the twelve-inch siphons, which cannot be drawn within the shell nor can the valves be completely closed. The anterior margin is slightly open for the extrusion of the foot.

A clam has neither head nor tentacles and but poorly developed sense perceptions. For these reasons the species that are too large for their shells would become the prey of innumerable enemies if they were not able to conceal themselves by burrowing.

Geoducks are considered delicious food but are not often in the markets because they are limited in their distribution and spoil easily, for the gaping shells do not conserve moisture well. Geoducks are being exterminated so rapidly that restrictions have been placed upon the number that can be taken.

CORRUGATED CLAM
Marcia kennerleyi

Two-thirds natural size

CORRUGATED CLAM
Marcia kennerleyi (Carpenter)

A STRIKING feature of this clam is the numerous, prominent lines of growth on the shell, which give it a corrugated appearance. Minute radial lines are visible near the beak, while fine flutings mark the inner edge of the shell. The shell is thick and hard and is a dull, gray color. It measures approximately two and one-half inches in length and one and three-fourths inches in width. Three large teeth and a strong external ligament form the hinge. The interior of an empty shell shows clearly the points of attachment of the abductor muscles and the pallial line where the mantle was fastened to the shell.

The shape and structure of clam shells depend upon the manner of life of the individual species. In the corrugated clam the abductor muscles lie towards the ends of the shell with the hinge half way between them. In this position they do an equal amount of work in opening and closing the shell. In other forms, like the mussels, the anterior muscle near the hinge does little labor and so the posterior muscle moves farther and farther from the hinge until it does nearly all the work of opening and closing the shell. In the corrugated clam the siphons are short, indicating that the clam lives near the surface for it must keep in contact with the outside world through the siphons. The shell is also tightly closed, which evidences its surface habits. This species has a small foot like all the shallow burrowing clams.

SUNSET CLAM

Psammobia californica

Two-thirds natural size

SUNSET CLAM
Psammobia californica Conrad

THE sunset shell, as one would expect from its name, is brilliantly colored. It is white with red rays extending from the beak to the margin, while fainter, concentric lines of red encircle the shell. A narrow band of brown skin borders the margin of the shell. The nearly central beak is small and flat and the two valves, held together by a short, thick hinge ligament, fit closely. The shell is long and flat and nearly equilateral and the surface is smooth except for tiny lines of growth. It is three inches long and one and three-fourths inches wide.

The shape of a clam has much to do with its burrowing habits. The sunset shell, which is thin and hatchet shaped, is admirably adapted for penetrating the sand. By a series of clever movements the clam digs so quickly that one has to drive a spade into the sand very rapidly to capture it. In contrast, the cockle shell is fat and nearly round and his difficulty in digging, so it lives just below the surface. In the cockle the ridges and other outgrowths on the shell serve to provide safe anchorage. The sunset clam is not common in our northern waters but farther south it is found in large numbers. It is interesting to study the environmental factors which limit the geographical distribution of animals.

PIDDOCK
Pholadidea penita

Natural size

PIDDOCK
Pholadidea penita (Conrad)

THIS animal burrows deeply into the sandstone rocks along the shore. The only part of the animal that projects from the hole is the long siphon through which food and water are brought to the clam. At the anterior end the shell is rounded but it tapers toward the posterior end, where it gapes sufficiently to allow for the extrusion of the siphon. The shell is covered with brown epidermis. Its length is from two to three inches.

Earlier students believed the boring to be the result of chemical action, but at present most scientists agree that the piddock bores by the rasping action of the shell, which in the young is provided with rows of spines or teeth toward the front end. The boring movements "consist chiefly of a twisting or turning of the whole shell on the fulcrum formed by the sucker-like foot and the four abductor muscles which are attached to the inner blades of the valves." The animal begins the process of home building early in life, so the opening of the burrow is comparatively small. In order to accommodate the growing body the clam is obliged to work constantly to enlarge the burrow. The deeply embedded anterior end of the shell is larger in diameter so once in the burrow the clam is imprisoned for life. When the animal is full grown and the burrow is complete, the foot degenerates and the shell grows over it and the abductor muscles.

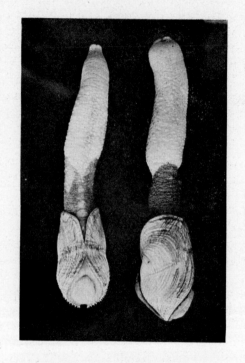

ROUGH PIDDOCK

Zirfaea gabbi

One-fourth natural size

ROUGH PIDDOCK
Zirfaea gabbi Tryon

THE rough piddock is a large clam that burrows into the hard clay along the shores. Its shell may be four inches long, two and one-half inches wide and two inches through. The shell only incompletely covers the animal and it gapes widely at both ends. At the anterior end the foot projects. This organ is oval in shape and flat on the ventral side and when the animal is boring the foot clings to the base of the burrow as a sucking disk. The foot and the abductor muscles furnish the motive power for the burrowing. From the posterior end of the shell the huge siphons project. These siphons are often nearly a foot long and one to two inches in diameter when extended. Even when retracted as far as possible they project far out of the shell. The shell is white, covered with a brown epidermis which also extends over the siphons for several inches.

A rough piddock's shell is well adapted for boring. About midway, the shell is obliquely divided by a deep furrow extending from the umbo to the basal margin. Posterior to the furrow the shell is marked by rough lines of growth but anterior to the furrow the growth lines are extremely rough and are crossed by longitudinal ribs which form sharp points. At the margin these ribs project as teeth which provide a rasping surface for digging.

Once in the hole the clam is imprisoned for life.

SHIP WORM OR TEREDO

Bankia setacea

About natural size

SHIP WORM OR TEREDO
Bankia setacea Tryon

IN SPITE of its common name and naked worm-like body, the ship worm is a bivalve mollusk that has taken on an extraordinary mode of life. For protection it bores deep into pilings, wharfs, and the hulls of wooden ships. In so doing it causes millions of dollars' worth of damage every year.

The opening of the burrow, made when the animal is young, is not larger than a pinhead, but farther in it may reach a diameter of seven-eighths inch and a depth of three feet. Once encased the ship worm can never leave its burrow.

The ship worm has a long naked body with a pair of small, peculiarly shaped shell valves at the anterier end and a pair of delicate siphons and feather-like pallets at the other end. The boring shells and the mouth lie at the inner end of the burrow while the siphons project from the open end. Water, bearing food particles, enters through one siphon and waste material, including the sawdust that has been cut away by the boring organs, is carried out by the other. No doubt, the animal obtains some nourishment from the wood as it passes through the digestive tract.

The complicated boring process is carried on by the action of the shell valves while the motive force is furnished by two pairs of muscles. The smooth burrow is lined with a calcareous secretion of the mantle. The end of the burrow can be closed by two hard pallets, situated at the sides of the siphons.

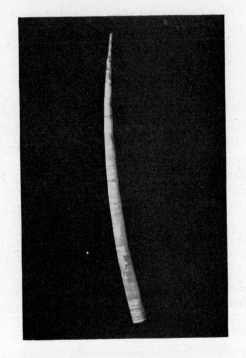

INDIAN TOOTH SHELL

Dentalium pretiosum

Two times natural size

INDIAN TOOTH SHELL
Dentalium pretiosum Sowerby

EMPTY tooth shells are frequently found on the beach, although living animals are in rather deep water. The tooth shell is extremely long and slender, shaped like an elephant's tusk, one and one-half to two inches in length and one-sixteenth to one-eighth inch in diameter. The shell is a hollow, slightly curved, white tube with fine rings and striations on the surface. There is a hole at each end and the shell is of slightly greater diameter at one end than at the other. This animal is highly modified and unlike any other mollusk. It has no head, no eyes, no gills, and no heart, but it is a mollusk because it has a foot, a radula, and a mantle that secretes the shell.

The animal digs into the sand with the foot and lies buried below low water mark. From the larger end of the shell extend the foot and also long filaments which serve in gathering the minute plants and animals on which the animal feeds. The posterior end of the shell projects up into the water and through it are conveyed both the incoming and outgoing currents of water. There are no special sense organs but the nervous system is well developed. The sexes are separate.

Tooth shells were the medium of exchange among the Indians of the Northwest until the arrival of Hudson's Bay Company, when shells were superseded by blankets. The Indians strung the shells on thin deer sinew both for money and ornaments. Perfect shells were more highly prized than worn ones.

231

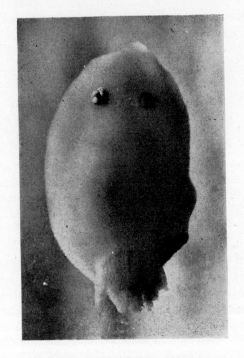

RED NUDIBRANCH

Rostanga pulchra

Four times natural size

RED NUDIBRANCH
Rostanga pulchra MacFarland

THE red nudibranch is abundant but it is difficult to see for it lives on red sponges and red algae. Everything conspires to make it inconspicuous for all the factors of the association are nearly identical in color. Even the ribbon egg masses of this nudibranch are the same brilliant red as the animal and its habitat.

A red nudibranch is a small animal, rarely growing larger than one-half to three-fourths inch in length, one-third inch in width and one-fourth inch in height. Its body is elliptical with the ends equally rounded. An ample mantle covers the whole body except at the posterior tip of the foot. The foot, which is rounded in front and pointed at the back, is a lighter red than the upper surface. In some specimens the dorsal surface is dotted with minute brown or black spots. Near the anterior end of the body are two short, stout tentacles (rhinophores), and near the posterior end are ten or twelve branchial plumes arranged in a circle. These plumes are slightly lighter in color than the dorsal surface of the animal, and they can be completely retracted within the sheath. Like the snails, the nudibranchs have a radula— a rasping tongue-like organ with many teeth—to tear up the food.

For brilliance of color patterns and variations in form, nudibranchs are unequalled by any other class of marine animals. Every color of the rainbow is appropriated by the nudibranch.

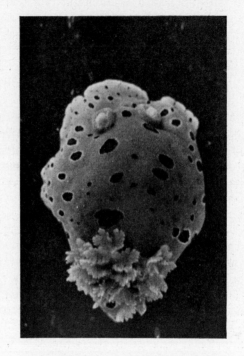

RINGED NUDIBRANCH
Diaulula sandiegensis

Natural size

RINGED NUDIBRANCH
Diaulula sandiegensis Cooper

The ringed nudibranch is found in rocky tide pools in the fucus zone. A large specimen measures two and one-half inches in length and one inch in width. This species is readily recognized by the soft, elliptical body marked with dark brown or black rings arranged in two irregular rows on either side of the back. The general color of the back is a pale yellow or brown, with tiny elevations which give a velvety appearance. A notched mantle entirely covers the animal. At the anterior end the foot is divided into two lobes.

Dorsal tentacles (rhinophores) project at the anterior end of the body and a rosette of six deeply plumed gills is situated near the posterior end. Both tentacles and gills can be completely drawn into the body sheath. The anal opening is in the branchial rosette.

Nudibranchs make use of the mucous secretion given off by the flattened foot to aid them in locomotion. Most nudibranchs have no swimming appendages but reach the surface of the water with the aid of seaweed or other material support. On reaching the top of the water many nudibranchs secrete layers of mucous which form threads, and suspended by them the animals hang in inverted positions several inches below the surface. The thread is made by bringing the head and foot together and the animal reaches different depths in the water by transferring the point of attachment and by secreting a longer thread (Flattely and Walton).

235

SEA LEMON

Anisodoris nobilis

One-half natural size

SEA LEMON
Anisodoris nobilis MacFarland

THE COMMON name indicates that this nudi-branch, found in rocky pools or on piles at low tide, resembles a lemon. It has a large, plump body, sometimes measuring five inches in length, two and one-half inches in width, and one inch in height, and is elliptical in shape with nearly equally rounded ends. The general ground color is a rich yellow, varying to light yellow in some specimens. On the dorsal surface are numerous tubercles that give the animal a warty appearance. Mottled everywhere, between the tubercles are irregular, black or dark brown blotches. Two thick, horn-like tentacles, called rhinophores, are situated near the anterior end, while at the posterior end are six branched, plumed gills that spread out into a beautiful, feathery rosette nearly covering the back of the sea lemon. When the animal is touched the tentacles and branched plumes are quickly and completely withdrawn. The mantle extends far beyond the foot, except at the back of the animal. The large adhesive foot is flat and smooth and is a lighter color than the dorsal surface. In front of the foot is the small mouth and a pair of oral tentacles.

This animal lays its eggs in a beautiful, yellow ribbon about an inch wide and eight to ten inches long, the edges of which are fluted in a most graceful manner. Minute eggs are scattered through the gelatinous ribbon. Nudibranchs are hermaphroditic—male and female organs in the same animal.

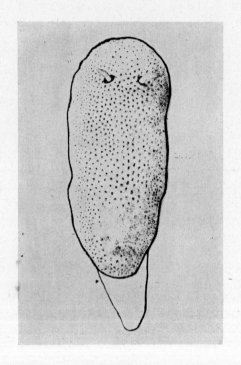

(Picture taken from MacFarland)

YELLOW NUDIBRANCH

Cadlina marginata

Slightly enlarged

YELLOW NUDIBRANCH
Cadlina marginata MacFarland

THIS nudibranch is about two inches long and one inch wide and is a clear, translucent yellow-white color. The body is elliptical, less broadly rounded behind than in front. It is covered everywhere on the dorsal surface with low tubercles, each one tipped with lemon yellow and surrounded with a narrow ring of white. Upper and lower margins of the mantle are bordered with a narrow band of lemon yellow. The tips of the dorsal tentacles and the six plumed gills arranged in an incomplete circle are also yellow. Wide mantle margins ex'end far beyond the narrow foot except at the posterior end.

Nudibranch egg masses have a distinct pattern for each family, although all of them are in coils or ribbons held together by mucous. The width of the egg ribbon is dependent upon the width of the mantle margins. The egg jelly is compressed between the foot and the mantle and the markings of the edges of the ribbon are similar to the undulations of the mantle margin. It seems that the eggs are transferred from the ovary to the mantle margin by the sole gland of the foot before the closure and placement of the ribbon. No precaution is taken to conceal the egg masses, perhaps, because of the great number of eggs they contain. Darwin calculated that in a ribbon twenty inches long there are 600,000 eggs. Fortunately, only a small percentage hatches.

(Picture taken from MacFarland)

BROWN NUDIBRANCH

Acanthodoris brunnea

Three times natural size

BROWN NUDIBRANCH
Acanthodoris brunnea MacFarland

IT IS difficult to realize that a nudibranch is a snail, because its plump, highly arched body above and the broad, flat foot below are not at all like those of a typical snail.

The brown nudibranch measures approximately one inch in length, one-half inch in width, and one-third inch in height. Covering the dorsal surface everywhere are thickly set conical tubercles with rounded tips. There is no definite arrangement of the tubercles except that smaller ones almost invariably alternate with larger ones. In general the color of the dorsal surface is brown flecked with irregular blotches of black. Between the tubercles are numerous small spots of light yellow and the mantle is edged with the same color.

Seven, wide-spreading plumes make up the branchial rosette, but the plumes cannot be retracted within the sheath. About ten tubercles are situated in the center of the incomplete branchial rosette and these enclose the anal papilla. The stalks of the branchial plumes are a yellow-brown marked on the inner side with lines of dark brown and tipped with lemon yellow. Two long, blue-black rhinophores stand erect near the anterior end of the body. These can be retracted within a low sheath.

The brown nudibranch is found under rocks on hard, sandy beaches. Nudibranchs have no protective covering nor defense equipment of any kind, so they must resort to the passive method of color adaptation.   241

GIANT NUDIBRANCH

Dendronotus giganteus

Two-thirds natural size

GIANT NUDIBRANCH
Dendronotus giganteus O'Donoghue

THE GIANT nudibranch is, undoubtedly, one of the strangest and most beautiful animals found in the inshore waters. When swimming it is a gorgeous creature, swaying gracefully from side to side, but if it is stranded on the beach it is shapeless and difficult to recognize.

This large nudibranch sometimes attains a length of eight and a width of three inches. It is variable in color, but is frequently a soft gray, with the side branches of the dorsal cerata a dark brown-gray with purple or white tips. A narrow white stripe encircles the margin of the foot. "There are no tentacles, but in their place are two antler-like appendages pointing forward and branched like a tree. All along the back are two rows of these curiously branched processes which give the animal the appearance of a plant. These cerata or dorsal papillae (appendages) are delicately transparent, contractile, and richly colored. The function of these papillae is not fully known. As the animal has no specialized breathing organs, it is reasonable to suppose that respiration is carried on through the outer skin and perhaps over the surface of these branched papillae. The liver, which in most nudibranchs is extremely large and completely surrounds the stomach, in *Dendronotus* also extends into the dorsal cirri (cerata), so they may have some sort of digestive function" (Augusta Arnold, *Sea Beach at Ebb Tide*).

HOODED NUDIBRANCH

Melibe leonina

Two-thirds natural size

HOODED NUDIBRANCH
Melibe leonina (Gould)

THE HOODED nudibranch is a most unusual
species that is commonly found on eel grass and
occasionally on other marine plants. This nudibranch is from three to four inches long and one
inch wide, and the body covering is so thin and
transparent that all the internal organs can be seen
through it. Its most characteristic feature is the
hood which surrounds the head and opens on the
lower side. When the animal is searching for food
the hood is distended widely and then contracted
into a knob when food is obtained. The hood is
held in a direct position for the capture of horizontally swimming creatures. The hooded nudibranch
is a voracious feeder; its stomach has been found
so completely filled with minute animals that the
body bulged in an almost perfect sphere. The
hood also serves in floating the animal. On the
upper side of the hood are two ear-like flaps and
on the dorsal surface of the body are inflated leaf-
like appendages or cerata, which gradually become
smaller toward the posterior end.

A hooded nudibranch does not use the poorly
developed foot much, for it is in almost constant
motion, swimming dorsal side downward with the
head and tail nearly touching one another.

Egg masses of this species are deposited in
spiral ribbons one to one and one-half inches in
width and three or four inches in length. A strong
offensive odor is given off when the animal is
touched and it feigns death most cleverly.

OPALESCENT NUDIBRANCH

Hermissenda crassicornis

About natural size

OPALESCENT NUDIBRANCH
Hermissenda crassicornis Eschscholtz

NUDIBRANCHS are called sea slugs, for they are closely related to the common garden slugs. Nudibranchs are marine slugs that have no shells in adult life, but they show their true affinity to the mollusks by having shells in the embryonic stage.

The opalescent nudibranch is probably the most abundant nudibranch on our coasts, where it is found on stones, eel grass, pilings and in tide pools. It is a beautiful species with many long, plume - like projections on the dorsal surface. These projections, which are called cerata and take the place of gills, are a red-brown color with a bright red spot at the tip of each. Much iridescence shows at the base of the cerata and on the edges of the body. The cerata cover the entire back of the animal except for an open space down the middle. This species of nudibranch measures one to two inches in length, and one-half inch in width, but it contracts and expands so greatly that it may be twice or half that length. Two sets of long tentacles move around constantly. The tentacles around the mouth apparently have considerable power of discrimination in taste and smell, but the dorsal tentacles do not have this ability. An opalescent nudibranch swims about in an inverted position.

In spring the opalescent nudibranch lays its eggs in a gelatinous cord-like ribbon and hangs it over a rock or on eel grass.

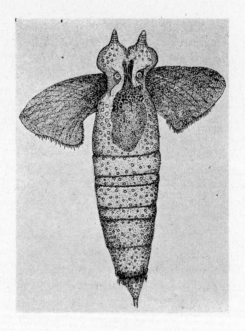

(Picture taken from Agersborg)

SEA ANGEL

Clione kincaidi

Four times natural size

SEA ANGEL
Clione kincaidi Agersborg

SEA ANGELS are dainty, translucent little creatures which swim vertically through the water by flapping their large wings. Sea angels usually swim in schools far out at sea. Only rarely do they come close to the shore. They respond to light and warmth, so rise to the surface during the day and sink to great depths at night.

A sea angel is a mollusk which has no shell and the foot is modified into wing-like appendages. A good sized specimen is about an inch long and one-fourth inch wide, tapering to a point at the posterior end. The head, one-sixth the length of the body, is divided into two lobes with the mouth between them. The fins or wings arise from a short neck. Muscle bands in the wings give them a diamond-like design. On the ventral side of the neck and between the wings are the remnants of the foot. The translucent body is marked off by four to six horizontal muscle bands; the posterior sixth of the body, which may or may not be red, is separated by a hairy groove. A bright red liver, with the heart at the left, fill one-third of the visceral cavity. The entire surface of the animal is studded with circular, oblong or conic bodies. These are densest near the posterior end. The body is covered with vibrating hairs, "which give the organism gentle, progressive movements, though it is otherwise at rest" (Agersborg).

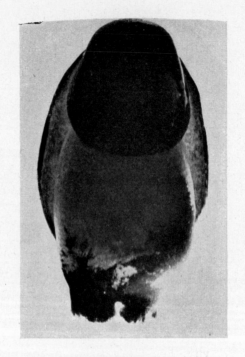

WHITE BUBBLE SNAIL

Haminoea vesicula

Four times natural size

WHITE BUBBLE SNAIL
Haminoea vesicula Gould

WHITE BUBBLE snails are found on mossy rocks, in tide pools and on eel grass. The small shell is rounded and consists of but one large body whorl for the spire is sunken and compressed. It has a broadly oval aperture as long as the shell and the outer lip is sharp. The shell is so thin and fragile that it seems to be of little use to the animal it only partially protects. When in motion the yellow-brown body of the animal extends so far beyond the shell that it is entirely covered. The shell itself measures one-third inch in length and one-fifth inch in diameter but when the snail is fully extended it may reach a length of more than an inch and a diameter of a half inch. In color, the shell is a pale green-yellow with many minute lines and is covered with a thin cuticle. In especially light colored specimens the pulsations of the heart can be seen through the shell. Egg masses of *Haminoea vesicula* are coiled yellow gelatinous ribbons about two inches long and one-third inch wide, attached to eel grass.

There is a black bubble snail, *Haminoea solitaire*, which differs from the white bubble snail by having a black body and living in the mud where it plows along just under the surface. Eggs of *Haminoea solitaire* are abundant upon the sand where they look like small balloons of soft colorless gelatin. Within the masses of gelatin are many tiny, white eggs.

OLIVE SNAIL

Olivella boetica

Five times natural size

OLIVE SNAIL
Olivella boetica Carpenter

THIS INTERESTING little snail is easy to identify because of its beauty but it is rare. Olive snails live in groups and can generally be traced by the tiny canals they form as they crawl along just beneath the surface of the sand. The shell is cylindrical, tapering at both ends. The spire is short and the body whorl very large, composing most of the shell. A long, narrow aperture, the length of the body whorl, allows for the protrusion of the animal's large foot. The foot is divided into two long lobes which curve back over the shell, nearly covering it. By using the foot as a sort of plow the animal pushes itself through the sand. The shell measures up to one inch in length and one-third inch in diameter. Its color is a red-brown or gray with irregular white patches and lines; the entire surface is highly polished and porcelain-like. This animal seems to be a degenerate form for it has neither eyes nor tentacles.

Olive shells have always been favorites among collectors, especially in the tropics, where there are many species. Only one or two species are found on our temperate Pacific Coast shores. Strings of olive shells are found in graves and mounds of Indians by whom they were used as ornaments and money. These shells are easy to thread because the animal absorbs the hard internal portion of the whorls until they become soft and pliable.

TABLED SNAIL

Chrysodomus tabulatus

Natural size

TABLED SNAIL
Chrysodomus tabulatus Baird

THE TABLED snail has a large, handsome shell with eight whorls. The shell varies in length from two to four inches and is from one and one-half to two inches in diameter. It has a high spire but the body whorl is considerably longer than the spire. A distinguishing feature of the shell is the distinct flat upper surface of the whorls, each forming a table. On the entire outer surface are spiral ridges of varying sizes. The canal is long and narrow and curves backward. There is a long, slender aperture with a thin outer lip and an encrusted inner lip. A thin, brown-green epidermis covers the outside of the shell while the inside is white and glistening. This snail lives below low water mark at a depth up to 150 feet but the shell is frequently thrown upon the shore during storms.

The egg cases of tabled snails are round, bright yellow chitinous capsules attached to rocks or dead shells. Twenty or more capsules, fastened by broad, short stalks, are arranged in a circular mass. Sometimes one capsule is placed upon another until a little mound is formed. Numerous, tiny eggs are in each capsule but only a few ever mature, for while still in the capsule the stronger, more active larvae eat the weaker ones. The surviving larvae leave the capsule by breaking a small hole in the inturned, flattened side. "This is struggle to the death at the very threshold of life. Many are called but few are chosen to survive" (Thomson, *Haunts of Life*).

255

SPINDLE SNAIL

Searlesia dira

Two times natural size

SPINDLE SNAIL
Searlesia dira Reeve

THIS SNAIL has a spindle shaped shell marked from apex to base with conspicuous, elevated ridges. The spire is high, the apex acute and the whorls rounded; the body whorl is not much longer than the spire and the aperture is shorter than the spire. There are nine longitudinal ridges upon the whorls of the spire. The shell recurves slightly at the base showing a prominent umbilicus or groove and definite notches mark the interior of the aperture. Both externally and internally the shell is a dull brown color overwashed with white. An average sized shell measures one and one-half inches in length and three-fourths inch in height. It is one of the most graceful shells on our shores and is plentiful on rocks at low tide.

The seashore offers great advantages over the depths of the ocean for animal life but it also has drawbacks. The violence of the waves destroys some of the inhabitants; the retreating tide exposes them to enemies and to changes in their living conditions generally. Hence, there have arisen various forms of adaptation designed to bring about the "survival of the fittest." The mollusks have solved this problem better, perhaps, than any other group of animals, through the development of hard shells. This self-preservation is further sought by the sand burrowing, rock boring, and rock clinging habits of the clams and snails.

WRINKLED SNAIL

Amphissa columbiana

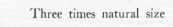

Three times natural size

WRINKLED SNAIL
Amphissa columbiana Dall

THIS SNAIL has a slender shell with a high spire which ends in a comparatively acute apex. Seven distinct convex whorls make up the shell and each whorl is marked longitudinally with eighteen or twenty wavy, rounded ridges which extend from suture to suture. On the body whorl spiral lines are also visible. The aperture is rather wide, the inner lip is thickened and the outer lip is smooth and thin. Externally, the shell is a light tan color and internally, it is white and shiny. Its length is one inch and its diameter one-third inch. It is found on rocky shores.

The sense of touch is well developed in all parts of the snail's body but it is especially delicate in the tentacles. Snails are also sensitive to odors for they respond quickly to bait that has a strong scent. Otocysts, resembling organs of hearing, are usually present in the feet of mollusks and these enable them to maintain their equilibrium and sense of direction. Most snails have a pair of eyes, in some species they are located at the base of the tentacles while in others they are at some distance out on them. These eyes range from small depressions in the skin lined with pigmented cells to highly specialized organs of vision having "an eyeball" enclosing a sort of lens.

The area between the high and low tide marks and the shallow water just below the beach were undoubtedly the early scenes of development of plant and animal life.

LEAFY HORNMOUTH SNAIL

Purpura foliata
with egg cases

Slightly reduced

LEAFY HORNMOUTH SNAIL
Purpura foliata (Martyn)

THE LEAFY hornmouth is one of the most striking snails on our shores. It is recognized at once by the three broad, wing-like projections which seem to be made up of overlapping plates, running longitudinally along the shell. A rather short spire is not definitely marked off from the body whorl. Heavy spiral ribs encircle the whorls and spread out fan-like over the wings. There is a distinct projection at the base of each wing and also a sharp point near the lower edge of the outer lip of the nearly circular aperture. The shell measures about three inches in length and one and three-fourths inches in diameter including the wings; its color is usually white overwashed with brown or marked with brown bands.

The animal frequently deposits a cluster of egg capsules upon its own shell, or they may be placed on rocks. Twenty-five or more eggs are enclosed in each bright yellow, stalked, chitinous case which has the shape of the calyx of a calla lily.

An interesting fact about snails is their lack of symmetry. Crabs, clams, segmented worms, and fish are symmetrical—a line drawn through the middle divides the animal into similar halves—but through some curious evolutionary process the internal organs of snails are twisted to one side and folded upon themselves until the arrangement of the organs is highly complex. One wonders whether the spiral shell is the cause or the result of this distortion.

261

WRINKLED PURPLE SNAIL

Thais lamellosa

One and one-half times natural size

WRINKLED PURPLE SNAIL
Thais lamellosa (Gmelin)

THE MOST casual observer on the beach notices the myriads of wrinkled purple snails clinging to the barnacle strewn rocks or creeping about in the tide pools. This snail has an attractive shell and its great diversity of markings and colorings make it a never-ending source of interest for the seashore naturalist.

The wrinkled snail always has a thick, heavy shell and the body whorl has from nine to twenty ridges elevated and wrinkled at the edges marking the lines of growth. Some shells have a comparatively smooth exterior and others are exceedingly rough. On the rocks exposed to surf the shells are quite smooth, in order, no doubt, to offer as little resistance as possible to the rushing waters. The forms on the open coast have short spires and wide apertures. On the sheltered beaches elongated, deeply ribbed forms with small apertures are found. All shells shade from white through yellow to dark brown and may be either plain or banded. Inside, the shell is pearly white with tooth-like indentations on the outer edge of the opening. A shell of average size measures two inches in length and one and one-fourth inches in diameter.

The wrinkled purple snail is carnivorous in its food habits and eats young ascidians, oysters, barnacles and even its own egg capsules. It is unable to attack thick shelled animals like clams.

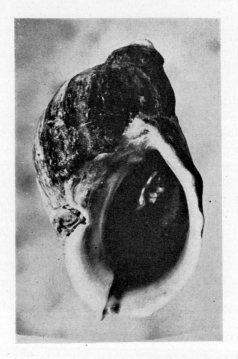

SHORT SPIRED PURPLE SNAIL

· Thais emarginata

Three times natural size

SHORT SPIRED PURPLE SNAIL
Thais emarginata (Deshayes)

NUMEROUS SHORT spired purple snails cling to the under side of rocks where the waves beat high. An average sized shell is about an inch long and three-fourths inch wide and it may be a dull gray or brown color but like other members of the genus shows much color variation depending on the mode of life. The exterior of the shell is rough with indistinct ribs; the interior of the shell opening is brown but the flaring lip and columella are white. A conspicuous feature of the shell is the short, thick spire of the three whorls. The body whorl is large and well rounded. A dark brown operculum closes over the opening of the shell when the animal desires privacy. Purple shells usually remain attached to rocks during low tide but sometimes they suddenly relax their hold and drop into the tide pools beneath.

When purple shells are broken or injured they give off a reddish-purple dye. The ancient Romans used this dye as the basis of the famous "Tyrian Purple." They gathered large quantities of the snails, placed them in mortars and ground them up. It is said that when a garment was placed in this mixture it received a rich purple hue. Apparently, we do not employ the same methods in extracting the dye that the Romans used because we find it very difficult to get a brilliant, clear color from the snail shell dye.

UNIFORM PURPLE SNAIL

Thais Lima

Two times natural size

UNIFORM PURPLE SNAIL
Thais lima (Martyn)

THE shell of the uniform purple snail has alternate large and small spiral ridges. The shell is moderately arched with a sharp, short spire; the outer lip of the aperture is thin and fluted. A narrow canal curves to the left and a horny operculum closes the aperture. This species exhibits every shade of color from white to dark brown, and the background is sometimes ornamented with darker bands. Its size is approximately one and one-half inches long and one inch wide.

Egg capsules of the purple snails are interesting objects which are common on the beaches in early spring. They have the appearance of grains of oats and adhere to rocks, shells or pieces of wood. The capsules, called sea oats, are placed either in circular or longitudinal masses by the snail moving forward a short distance after each capsule has been deposited. Each capsule is an elongated vase-like parchment case mounted on a slender stalk. A capsule contains a varying number of eggs. A single animal has been known to deposit 245 capsules. Even before the tiny snails emerge from the cases they are cannibalistic, the stronger ones eating the weaker until only a small percentage survives. When the surviving larvae have reached a certain stage of development they emerge from the top of the capsule. "Sea oats" are the egg cases of *Thais lamellosa*, but the egg cases of all species of purple snails resemble similar cereal grains.

WHELK OR OREGON TRITON

Argobuccinium oregonensis

Two-thirds natural size

WHELK OR OREGON TRITON
Argobuccinium oregonensis Redfield

THE whelk is a snail three or four inches in length and two inches in diameter that is sometimes found on the beach but is more common in deep water. If alive, a bristly, coarse epidermis entirely covers the shell. These bristles are arranged in spiral rows around the shell. In addition to the bristles, numerous hydroids, tube worms or barnacles may adhere to the shell. An empty shell loses the epidermis and one sees that it has seven or eight whorls marked with longitudinal and transverse ribs. A latticed effect is produced by the ridges. At the base of the large, convex body whorl the canal flares as if another whorl were being formed.

The whelk is an excellent form in which to study the internal structure of a snail for parts of the body extend far out of the shell. The soft parts—foot, tentacles, mouth and siphon are a red-purple color with many brown spots. Long stout tentacles wave and stretch in all directions and small black eyespots can be seen located at the bases of them. A small slit-like mouth with fleshy lips is situated on a short proboscis below the tentacles. Snails that have proboscides are apparently always carnivorous. With the proboscis the animal can reach into the interior of the shell of its victim and devour the soft body parts. The siphon, which carries in water to supply the gills, protrudes from the flared end of the canal. The gills lie just back of the siphon.

SEA CORN

Egg Cases of Argobuccinium oregonensis

Natural size

SEA CORN
Egg Cases of Argobuccinium oregonensis

THE egg cases of this snail are so unusual in appearance that they deserve a story of their own. Unless a seashore naturalist is somewhat familiar with the egg capsules of snails he would not associate them with the adult animals.

Like the egg cases of several other snails these resemble cereal grains. Those of the whelk are shaped like kernels of corn and are of much the same size and texture. Circular masses of capsules about four inches in diameter are deposited by the snail on the under side of stones or on old wharf piling. These masses are made by the snail moving slowly in a circular route and depositing the eggs at regular intervals. The snail begins the placement in the center and works outward. Great numbers of eggs can be seen within each transparent capsule. As the eggs begin to hatch into larvae they turn upon one another, the leaders eating the laggards, until only a few are left in each capsule. The surviving larvae escape through a hole in the outer edge of the capsule. They swim about for a time in the sea and then shells are secreted and the animals settle down to the sluggish life of snails.

"Master, I marvel how the fishes live in the sea,
Why, as men do a-land; the great ones eat up the
little ones."—Shakespeare.

THREADED OR SCREW SNAIL

Bittium eschrichtii

Four times natural size

THREADED OR SCREW SNAIL
Bittium eschrichtii Middendorff

THE threaded or screw snail has a small, tur-
reted shell which is found on rocks, on wiry grasses
of salt marshes, or on algae at tide mark. On the
shell are nine whorls, each of which is slightly
smaller than the one below until the apex is
sharply acute. The whorls are separated by deep
spiral grooves and on each whorl are four flattened
ridges. An oval aperture extends the length of the
last whorl. A screw shell is either white or brown
and measures three-fourths inch in length and one-
eighth inch in diameter.

Many students of biology think that the nitri-
fying bacteria were the earliest forms of life because they alone are capable of deriving their energy and nutrition from inorganic chemical com-
pounds and are independent of other forms of life
and of the sun. Some students believe that the be-
ginnings were in deep water; some think that the
moist earth and terrestrial waters containing nitro-
gen were the original homes of animals; the others seek to prove that fresh waters were essential
for the production of life. Almost all scientists
agree that air and water were both essential. The
seashore offers this exchange of air and water
more favorably than do other habitats. Geologic
history traces marine animals similar to present day
forms back 25,000,000 years. Probably through a
gradual transition marine animals have become
fresh water forms, land dwellers and tree resi-
dents.

CHECKERED HAIRY SNAIL

Trichotropis cancellata

Three times natural size

CHECKERED HAIRY SNAIL
Trichotropis cancellata Hinds

THE SHELL of this snail is oblong with a sharply pointed apex; the seven whorls are separated by a deep line and the spire is almost as long as the body whorl. Strong spiral ribs which are crossed by fainter longitudinal lines checker the entire surface. The aperture is rounded and an extremely short canal extends from the inner lip. Outside, a light brown or gray hairy fringe grows on the spiral ribs. Within, the shell is white and highly polished. The shell measures one inch in length and one-half inch in width.

The checkered hairy snail has a distinct head, which bears a pair of tentacles. Eyes are on the outer side at the base of the tentacles. The siphon, which is an elongation of the mantle fold, is short.

The power of regeneration is developed in mollusks only to a slight degree. The enclosure of a mollusk within a strong house protects it somewhat against injury but if the shell is damaged it can be repaired with deposits of lime by the mantle. If the shell was originally colored, the repaired portion does not have the same color, showing, perhaps, that the repair work was done by another part of the mantle. Mollusks can regrow a portion of a foot, a lost eye or a tentacle. Certain species are said to deliberately amputate an injured member if it is hurt beyond repair.

LEAN BASKET SNAIL

Alectrion mendicus

Five times natural size

LEAN BASKET SNAIL
Alectrion mendicus Gould

SNAIL shells show such varieties of shape, color and sculpturing that they are admired and gathered all over the world. Our northern species are not as large or as brilliant as the more tropical forms but some of ours are most attractive.

The lean basket snail is a dainty little species measuring about one inch in length and one-third inch in width. It is covered with raised spiral threads and seven prominent longitudinal ridges. The shell has six or seven whorls, all of which are elongated; the last whorl is a little more than half the length of the shell. The somewhat thickened, rounded opening is not more than one-third the length of the shell. Within, the shell is white with a salmon colored tooth or notch. This opening can be securely closed by a horny door attached to the foot. When alive the shell is a dull brown, when dry it is ash colored.

The spiral shape of the snail shell forces a displacement of the organs so that one member of each pair is usually missing—there being only one gill, one kidney, one auricle and one olfactory organ. Snails have well developed nervous systems and special sense organs. The sense organs consist of a pair of eyes, one or two pairs of tentacles, which serve as feelers and olfactory organs, and a pair of equilibrium organs located in the foot.

PERIWINKLE OR SITKA LITTORINE

Littorina sitchana

Five times natural size

PERIWINKLE OR SITKA LITTORINE
Littorina sitchana Philippi

PERIWINKLES attached to rocks, pilings, fucus and eel grass, swarm along the rocky shores. The Sitka periwinkle has a small, strong spiral shell with three convex whorls and five indistinct spiral ridges mark each whorl. The shell rarely exceeds one-half inch in height and one-third inch in diameter and it has a nearly circular aperture. Though there is much color variation, many periwinkles are chocolate brown spotted with white. A dark band usually borders the inside rim of the shell. Periwinkles show a protective resemblance in both form and color to the fucus, rocks or other backgrounds to which they adhere. For this reason they are hard to see.

This family of animals has an unusual foot. It is divided into two halves by a median line and the animal moves by first lifting one half and then the other.

Undoubtedly, the snail found highest up on the beach is the periwinkle or littorine. Most species are strictly between-the-tide animals and spend about the same length of time out of the water as in it. In fact, a periwinkle will die if permanently cut off from the air. Some species are said to live in trees overhanging the water where they are dashed by the spray. It would seem, therefore, that periwinkles are slowly becoming land animals. Many land animals were, undoubtedly, at one time marine forms. This change necessitates mainly the gradual substitution of lungs for gills.

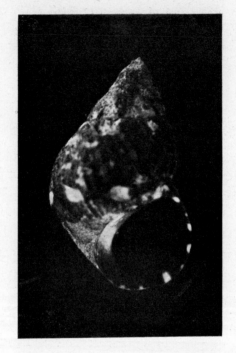

CHECKERED PERIWINKLE

Littorina scutulata

Six times natural size

CHECKERED PERIWINKLE
Littorina scutulata Gould

THE checkered periwinkle has a slender, pointed shell with the spire nearly half its height and the apex acute. There are four convex whorls on the shell and the aperture is not quite half the height of the shell. Most checkered periwinkles average one-half inch in height and one-fourth inch in diameter. The surface is frequently eroded and rough but when clear the color is brown with irregular bands and spots of white. Inside, the shell is a dark purple. Variations are so numerous that species are difficult to determine offhand.

A great many seashore animals react to the rhythmic behavior of the seashore—the ebb and flow of the tide and the alternation of darkness and light. Twice daily these animals are submerged in darkness and twice each day they are rocked with the up and down movements of the tides. In *Littorina* this tidal rhythm persists after the external stimuli have been removed. Even in the laboratory the animals can be made active by rocking or shaking them but at periods corresponding to low tide one has to shake them longer to make them active. In other words, periods of inertia in the laboratory coincide with dry periods above the tide on the beach. This rhythmic response gradually weakens with the passage of time. The whole reaction is comparable to one's sense of rocking with the movement of a boat, even on land, after a long sea voyage (*The Biology of the Sea Shore*— Flattely and Walton).

WIDE CHINK SNAIL
Lacuna porrecta

Ten times natural size

WIDE CHINK SNAIL
Lacuna porrecta Carpenter

THE tiny *Lacuna,* or chink snail, is abundant on eel grass, and on the glades and holdfasts of the big kelps. The characteristic which distinguishes it is the umbilicus which forms a lengthened groove along the axis of the shell. A chink shell is minute, rarely becoming longer than one-fourth inch, or wider than one-eighth inch. Its shell is thin and cone-shaped and on it are five whorls, the top ones forming a depressed spire. The aperture is large and round. The color of the shell is yellow or brown marked with irregular brown bands and dots.

Egg masses of chinks are common on the eel grass and kelp. These are circular, light yellow gelatinous masses, one-eighth to one-fourth inch in diameter, with holes in the centers like doughnuts. Great numbers of individual eggs are enclosed in each yellow ring.

Snails have varied and interesting methods of egg production. Nature lovers are often puzzled by their strange chitinous capsules or gelatinous egg masses. In most species the snail larvae leave the capsules when they are in the veliger stage and swim about by means of hair-like structures which serve as oars. They swim until the adult form is reached; then they develop shells and settle down to the sluggish life of the snails. Snails that live high on the beach where the periods of drought are longer and the risks to free swimming larvae are greater emerge from the capsules as miniatures of the adults.

283

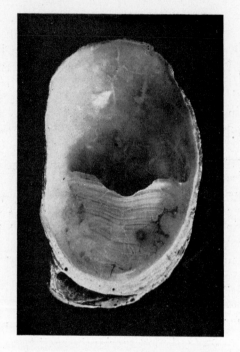

WHITE SLIPPER SNAIL
Crepidula nivea

Three times natural size

WHITE SLIPPER SNAIL
Crepidula nivea C. B. Adams

THE slipper snail, or boat snail, as it is sometimes called, adheres to rocks, to shells, to other
live mollusks or grows one upon another. It receives its name, slipper shell, from the pointed anterior end, the rounded posterior end and from the
shelf-like structure which partly covers the aperture. The shelf becomes a lateral partition and is
a certain identification mark of the group. A Chinese slipper into which one slips the foot furnishes
a good illustration of this shell. The shell is obliquely oval and convex above but may vary greatly
according to the nature of the surface to which it
adheres. Sometimes one can tell from the markings on the shell that the animal lived on a ribbed
shell when young and on a smooth one when old,
or vice versa.

An average sized shell measures one and one-
fourth inches long, three-fourths inch wide and one-
fourth inch high. Outside, the shell is a dull white,
probably tinged with brown. Inside, it is white and
glistening and the shelf is thin and delicate. The
small, inconspicuous apex is on the margin of the
shell and the spiral structure is nearly lost.

From its mode of life the slipper snail is inactive, apparently seldom or never straying from
the object that offers a secure holdfast, but if
forced to move it does so by means of its broad
foot.

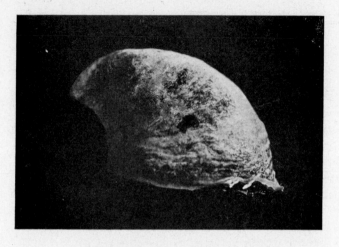

HOOKED SLIPPER SNAIL
Crepidula adunca

Three times natural size

HOOKED SLIPPER SNAIL
Crepidula adunca Sowerby

THIS slipper snail is distinguished by the prominent beak-like apex which curves backward and upward from the margin and by being slightly compressed on the sides. In color it is a dark brown with indistinct lighter bands and spots, and the whole shell is somewhat coarse and rough. Within, the shell is brown washed with a thin coating of white. The shelf divides the shell cavity nearly in the middle. This shell is three-fourth inch long, one-half inch wide, and one-half inch high. A hooked slipper snail attaches itself to rocks and shells as well as upon one another. When it is attached to rocks it appears much like a limpet.

Crepidula take special care of the young. The female constructs many little bags or capsules into each of which she puts about 250 eggs and then the cases are closed and fastened together by short cords. The whole mass is placed on the surface where the mother slipper snail happens to be sitting, on the under side of the shell or on the shelf. For about a month the mother guards the eggs and then holes begin to appear in the egg cases and the baby snails swim away from their parent. After a short free swimming period the young slipper snail settles down on some convenient stone for the rest of its life. All slipper snails are thought to be born males and after a period change into females. This is a strange and unusual type of development.

CHINESE HAT SNAIL

Calyptraea fastigiata

Four times natural size

CHINESE HAT SNAIL
Calyptraea fastigiata Gould

THE Chinese hat snail is a delicate little limpet-like form with the pointed apex nearly central. The shelf on the shell is attached on one side only; in the living animal the abductor muscle is attached to the shelf. This shell is circular, one-half inch high and three-fourths inch in diameter and has no spiral characteristics. Outside, the shell is white but it is partially covered by a thin, tan colored epidermis. Inside, the shell is white and glistening like the finest porcelain. This species lives in both deep and shallow water clinging with its broad foot to a stone or a shell. This and similar mollusks have the habit of growing one upon another; sometimes as many as five individuals are stacked up until the mass looks like a skyscraper.

An intensely interesting half hour may be spent in observing the animals found in a tide pool. Especially do the shells of crabs show a complex animal association. During a recent observation there were seen upon the carapace of a single crab, algae, a hydroid or two, a barnacle, and a tunicate; on the legs were a tube worm and a small Chinese hat snail; and under the abdomen, a parasitic crustacean. It is difficult to determine at what point such an association ceases to be for mutual benefit to the various members of the community and becomes harmful.

"And muse on Nature with a poet's eye."—Campbell.

MOON SNAIL

Polynices lewisii

About natural size

MOON SNAIL
Polynices lewisii (Gould)

THE moon snail is one of the most characteristic species on our sandy beaches where it lies partially buried in the sand. It has a strong, round, brown shell that is covered with a thin ashy skin. Lines of growth are indistinct. There are six convex whorls on the shell; the body whorl is much rounded and has a distinct, broad constriction about one-third of the distance down. The spire is low and broad. The opening of the shell is large and is tinged with a chestnut color inside. A medium sized moon snail measures three to four inches in length and has nearly the same diameter.

A moon snail has no eyes but has a keen sense of taste. The foot is enormous and when extended fits over the shell like a shield and with this it plows its way through the heavy, wet sand. One wonders how the immense foot can be drawn into the shell but if the animal is seized or irritated it quickly squeezes all the water out of the foot and draws it into the shell and tightly closes the door. The door is a horny operculum, or plate, situated on the dorsal side of the foot.

The moon snail is destructive to oyster beds because when burrowing for clams it suffocates the young oysters. It kills the clam by covering it with the huge foot or it may open the clam shell by drilling a hole into it.

SAND COLLAR OR MOON SNAIL
Polynices lewisii

One-half natural size

SAND COLLAR OR MOON SNAIL
Polynices lewisii (Gould)

A MOON snail has a curious egg case which frequently interests collectors on the beach. This egg case resembles a thin collar of sand and is just about large enough to go around one's neck. For a long time naturalists were greatly puzzled about this queer object and many humorous descriptions of it appeared in early zoological literature.

The snail secretes a large amount of mucous which is used to glue together particles of sand in the form of a collar with an opening on one side. This molding is apparently done over the large foot for it is of the same size and shape. In this slimy mass the animal deposits its eggs in a regular manner. The eggs are so minute that they cannot be distinguished from the sand grains and the whole structure looks like rough sand paper. In midsummer the eggs hatch out and the larvae swim about in the open water by means of cilia until the adult form is reached.

These sand collars are common on all shores where the moon snail lives.

> "So, naturalists, observe, a flea
> Has smaller fleas that on him prey;
> And these have smaller still to bite 'em;
> And so proceed—ad infinitum."—Swift.

BLACK TURBAN SNAIL
Tegula funebralis

Three times natural size

BLACK TURBAN SNAIL
Tegula funebralis (A. Adams)

THE shape of the turban snail reminds one of a turban which an Arab wraps around his head. In this species the body whorl is black or deep purple and the spire is low and depressed. Sometimes the covering of the apex is worn off so that a bright orange color can be seen. A characteristic feature of this species is the shirred effect at the upper edge of the body whorl. The top of the spiral ridges appear to be made of thin plate-like structures which form this shirring. The opening of the shell is large but it can be closed by a horny door. Inside, the shell is white with a narrow black band on the margin.

A turban snail moves about easily by means of the narrow foot. Between the shell and the foot the large head projects. The head is prolonged into a snout on which are two long tentacles. Two eyes, placed on short stalks, arise from the base of the tentacles. Long delicate filaments (cirri) extend beyond the shell when the animal is in search of food. These are sense organs which warn the snail of danger and do scouting duty.

The turban snail eats only seaweed which it scrapes off the rocks with its highly developed tongue (radula). It has no siphons. Snails with siphons are flesh-eating animals while those without siphons eat plants.

BLUE TOP SNAIL

Calliostoma costatum

Three times natural size

BLUE TOP SNAIL
Calliostoma costatum Martyn

THE blue top snail has an extremely beautiful, brightly colored, delicate shell. It is pyramidal in shape and the seven whorls are convex, each proportionately larger than the one above. The whorls are encircled by smooth spiral ribs of uniform width. From seven to nine ribs line the last whorl. The background of the shell is white with dark, chestnut brown ribs and the small, sharp pointed apex is usually a solid blue or purple color. Within, the shell is pearly and iridescent. A large, round aperture has a fluted margin. Only rarely does the shell become larger than three-fourths inch in height and three-fourths to one inch in diameter. The blue top is not a common shell but is sometimes found adhering to rocks at low tide mark or in shallow water.

For protective purposes the aperture of most snail shells is closed by a perfectly fitting horny operculum which is attached to the foot. The foot of a snail is long, broad and flat on the under side. This type of foot is produced by a thickening of the ventral body surface and it gives the animal the appearance of crawling on its stomach. There are many variations of a snail's foot depending upon the habitat and mode of life. Those living in sand have an extremely powerful foot which serves as a sort of plow; in some species the foot is like a fender and in others it is merely a sucking disk. Each species has a characteristic foot.

RINGED TOP SNAIL
Calliostoma annulatum (left)

VARIEGATED TOP SNAIL
Calliostoma variegatum (right)

Slightly enlarged

RINGED TOP SNAIL
Calliostoma annulatum Martyn

THE ringed top is, no doubt, the most colorful and the daintiest shell in this region. Its conical, fragile shell is made up of seven to nine flattened whorls. Each whorl is marked with small, beaded, spiral ridges. The shell itself is straw color, the beads are brown, and the lower edge of each whorl is outlined with a purple band. The acute apex is a solid purple color. Adding to the brilliancy of color is the salmon or orange colored foot which in a live specimen extends far out from the aperture. The ringed top may be slightly more than an inch in height and an inch in diameter. It is found on rocks or eel grass near the shore or in deep water. This fragile shell is easily broken by rough waves.

THE VARIEGATED TOP SNAIL
Calliostoma variegatum Carpenter

THIS species of snail closely resembles the ringed top but the shell is smaller and more pointed and the whorls are not flattened. The markings on the shell are similar but the purple color has been replaced by rose arranged in broken lines. This makes the color less brilliant than in the preceding species. The variegated top is usually found in deep water.

Breathing in snails is by means of gills which are bound together at their bases like the leaves of a book. Blood is conveyed to the gills by a large vessel. The blood is then forced through these thin leafy gills where it is purified.

MARGARITE SNAIL

Margarites pupillus

Three times natural size

MARGARITE SNAIL
Margarites pupillus Gould

THE Margarites are a group of attractive snails belonging to the same family as *Calliostoma*. Mrs. Oldroyd lists twelve species in this region but the distinctions between them are so minute and detailed that it is difficult for the amateur to differentiate them. To distinguish the genus is about all one can hope to do.

Margarites pupillus, the most common species, is found on eel grass and on the rocks in tide pools or in shallow water. The shell is pyramidal with a broad base. It is small, usually one-half to three-fourths inch in height and one-half inch in diameter. In color it is opalescent with green the predominating tint. Sometimes the iridescence is over-washed with a dull, lusterless white. The spire is elevated and the six whorls are convex. On the upper whorls are four or five circular ribs; on the body whorl are twelve ribs of decreasing width. The large, rounded aperture is iridescent within. A margarite has long, slender tentacles and the eyes are borne in short stalks. The animal has one gill, a short snout and usually frontal lobes on the head. A margarite is herbivorous, feeding only upon algae.

Some tropical members of this family are used extensively for ornaments. Shell covered boxes are made of these shells and one small opalescent species in the East Indies is polished and strung for necklaces.

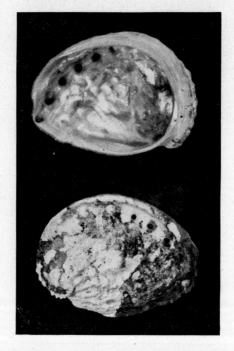

SMALL NORTHERN ABALONE
Haliotis kamtschatkana

One-half natural size

SMALL NORTHERN ABALONE
Haliotis kamtschatkana Linnaeus

THE only abalone found in the north is a small species averaging three to three and one-half inches in length and two to two and one-fourth inches in breadth and three-fourths to one inch in height. The opening of the shell is large and wide open. On the outside the shell is rough with conspicuous waved swellings. It is often encrusted with mineral deposits or is overgrown with vegetation. When the unattractive outer coverings are removed the shell is bright red and green. Along the left side of the shell is a series of prominent holes, four or five of which are open. These holes serve as breathing pores. Inside the holes is the respiratory chamber with two gills. The left edge of the shell is flattened and turned inward while the right side is simple. Within, the shell is beautifully colored. Iridescent and pearly hues give it a rainbow brilliance.

When the abalone is alive it is firmly attached to a rock by the large muscular foot which entirely fills the opening of the shell. To loosen an abalone from its foothold it is necessary to use a chisel. An abalone is vegetarian in its food habits. Sea weed is scraped from the rocks by the animal's rasping tongue.

The foot of the abalone is considered delicious for food.

The polished shells are widely used for ornaments or are made into buttons.

WHITE CAP LIMPET

Acmaea mitra

Three times natural size

WHITE CAP LIMPET
Acmaea mitra Eschscholtz

CERTAIN species of limpets are almost as common on our shores as are the barnacles. Children often call them Chinaman's hats or clown's pointed caps.

The white cap limpet has a heavy, white conical shell with an erect nearly central apex. No trace of the typical spiral snail shell is evident. Coralline algae often encrust the surface, giving it a green tinge. A large specimen measures one and one-fourth inches long, one inch high, and three-fourths inch wide. The limpet has such a powerful foot that it is quite impossible to tear it from a rock unless taken unawares. It has been estimated that a limpet with a basal area of one square inch requires a pull of seventy pounds to remove it.

A limpet is a vegetarian feeding only upon algae. It has no proboscis for only carnivorous or flesh eating forms are so equipped. The mouth is just in front of the foot and two long tentacles project beyond the shell. Just inside the lips is the pharynx, a muscular throat, which contains the jaws and radula. The jaws are used to bite off the food and the radula tears it into fine pieces. The radula is a long horny ribbon, the upper surface of which is covered with teeth in various shapes and numbers arranged in rows. By means of muscles the radula teeth can be raised or lowered so that they easily break up the food. Almost every species of snail has a characteristic radula pattern.

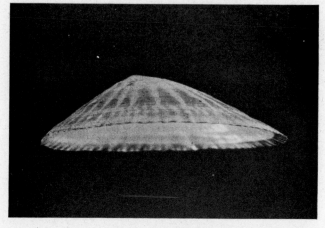

PLATE LIMPET

Acmaea scutum patina

Two times natural size

PLATE LIMPET
Acmaea scutum patina Eschscholtz

THIS limpet has a large, smooth, somewhat flattened, oval shell. The apex, situated near the middle, is low and rounded. Olive, gray, or black radiating lines mark the entire dorsal surface. Near the apex the lines are broken and irregular. Inside, the shell is a clear, blue-green color with a brown and white striped border. The shell extends some distance beyond the foot and the mantle edge. The plate limpet varies greatly in size but the proportion may be one inch long, three-fourths inch wide, and one-fourth inch high.

As in other mollusks the limpet shell increases in size by secretions of the mantle. This secretion is a liquid containing the shell matter in solution. Around the edge of the mantle is a complicated system of glands and pores from which this "stony liquid" is secreted. This liquid contains carbonate of lime and other inorganic materials which hardens when discharged. At the extreme edge of the mantle are the glands that secrete the epidermis that covers some mollusk shells. Pigment glands that give the color to the shell are also situated in the edges of the mantle. Periods of growth in mollusks are nearly always followed by periods of rest. During the inactive periods the animal thickens the edge of the shell to protect it against injury and when it begins to build again these thickened edges appear as raised lines of growth.

SHIELD LIMPET

Acmaea cassis pelta

Two times natural size

SHIELD LIMPIT
Acmaea cassis pelta (Eschscholtz)

THE shield limpet has a large oval shell the apex of which is conical and pointed and is placed a little in front of the middle. It has a strong shell with low ribs and on many shells the ribs, especially in front, are worn off. Outside, the shell is a gray-white with radiating black or brown stripes which are broken and uneven. Inside, the shell is pale green with a border or series of dark scallops. A large specimen is one and one-half inches long, one and one-fourth inches wide, and two-thirds inch high.

In a limpet shell the spire seems to be wholly absent and the entire shell consists of but one large body whorl. This shell covers the animal in a more or less conical, shield-like manner. Most embryonic limpet shells display a typical spiral plan but after hatching the animal does not build its house on the spiral design but expands the shell into a large shield. The lower side of the shell is entirely open and the broad foot of the animal almost fills the opening. This is apparently a successful device for by means of the foot the limpet clings desperately to the rock and it is far more securely anchored than an ordinary snail and therefore much safer from attack.

The sexes are separate in limpets and the young are hatched as free swimming larvae. Limpets are collected and sold as food in many parts of the world but in this region they are not used commercially.

MASK LIMPET

Acmaea digitalis

Three times natural size

MASK LIMPET
Acmaea digitalis Eschscholtz

THIS limpet is distinguished by the beaked apex which is anterior and forward pointing, and by the strong, rounded ribs on the shell. The front ribs may be worn away or obsolete. The area around the beak is often white or green and the outer edges of the shell are dark brown-green with inconspicuous white markings. Inside, the edges of the shell are fluted. A large specimen may measure one and one-half inches in length, one inch in width, and one-half inch in height.

A limpet glides about in search of food but always returns to its original home when the tide begins to ebb. The homing instinct of the limpet is strong and according to some writers (Ainsworth Davis) its "locality sense" is independent of any senses of sight, smell, or touch in the tentacles. The greatest distance a limpet has been known to wander from home is three feet but no matter in which direction it moves it always finds its way back. Definite scars on the rock mark the street and number of the limpet's home. The outline of the scar corresponds exactly to the shape of the shell so the limpet must always orient itself by facing in the same direction. The scar is made by the mechanical action of the foot surface and the beveled edge of the shell. Scientists have not yet discovered where the seat of the limpet's marvelous sense of direction lies. The trail of slime which it leaves behind when it moves may help it in retracing its path.

ROUGH KEYHOLE LIMPET

Diadora aspera

One and one-fourth times natural size

ROUGH KEYHOLE LIMPET
Diadora aspera (Eschscholtz)

THE rough keyhole limpet has a high arched shell with a small, nearly circular hole in the apex. The hole is situated a little in front of the center of the shell. Dark gray lines on a dirty white background radiate from the apex and the whole structure is marked by minute concentric lines. Fine notches mark the margin of the shell. Inside, the shell is smooth and white. In size the rough keyhole limpet is approximately one and one-half inches long and one inch wide. The keyhole serves to carry off the outgoing water and in this way the water taken in through the paired gills is kept free from waste material.

The keyhole limpet clings to rocks where the flat foot exerts a tremendous pull. When in search of food the foot releases the hold and the animal glides about; from beneath the shell two tentacles do scouting duty. A limpet is a vegetarian and eats seaweed which is scraped off the rocks with the rasping tongue. The limpet's tongue is nearly twice as long as the animal and on the tongue are great numbers of teeth arranged in transverse rows. The teeth vary in shape but those on either side of the center correspond each to each. Those in front tend to become worn away by constant use and to replace them new ones are formed at the other end of the radula. The form of the teeth is an index to the diet of animals.

RIBBED KEYHOLE LIMPET
Puncturella cucullata

Two and one-half times natural size

RIBBED KEYHOLE LIMPET
Puncturella cucullata Gould

THE ribbed keyhole limpet is oval at the base, rising to a high pointed cone. The curved apex is so far back on the shell that the posterior slope is nearly vertical. There is a long, narrow keyhole, hardly more than a slit, on the posterior slope of the apex. On the surface are about forty prominent ribs which are alternately large and small. The outside of the shell is a dirty white but the inside is clear and glistening, and the margin is beautifully notched. An average size for the ribbed keyhole limpet is one inch long, three-fourths inch high and three-fourths inch wide.

The shell of a limpet is simply a shield-like covering with only a suggestion of the spiral form at the tip of the apex, but in the embryo stages the limpet has a shell which coils over the head. Most of the internal organs of a limpet are paired and arranged in a normal manner.

Snails show great variety in shapes of shells and it is not possible to say how great a part environment or other forces may have played in their development. The conical shape of the limpet shell is admirably adapted to withstand the battering action of the tides and stones thrown upon it. Limpets are considered more primitive than the true snails. As might be expected land snails have much thinner shells than do marine species.

OPALESCENE SQUID

Loligo opalescens

One-fourth natural size

OPALESCENE SQUID
Loligo opalescens Berry

SQUIDS are distinguished from devil fish by having ten arms instead of eight and by having a long, cylindrical mantle that tapers to a point. On the posterior end of the mantle are two long, triangular fins. The mantle measures six to eight inches and the arms are more than half that length. Extending the length of the mantle is a thin, cartilaginous pen that holds it rigid. This pen is concealed within the skin and is all that is left of the mollusk shell. All the internal organs and the ink sac are enclosed within the mantle. There are two powerful, chitinous jaws in the pharynx. Large, highly developed eyes are on each side of the head.

The arms of the squid are thick and unequal in length; one pair, used in grasping, is very long and has four rows of sucking disks near the ends. The other arms have two rows of concave, horny suckers extending the entire length. Along the sucker bearing surface of all the arms is a delicate membranous web which aids in swimming. The siphon is on the ventral surface just in front of the mantle. It is a muscular tube through which water is expelled and which aids in steering the animal. A squid darts through the water with great rapidity.

The eggs of this squid are embedded in white capsules about two inches long, anchored in great clusters to a rock or other solid object.

OCTOPUS OR DEVIL FISH

Polypus hongkongensis

One-half natural size
Young specimen about one-fourth grown

OCTOPUS OR DEVIL FISH
Polypus hongkongensis Hoyle

THE octopus is a first cousin of the snails and clams. Its mantle, radula, and arrangements of the internal organs place it with the mollusks, but it is far superior to them in organization and brain development.

Most of our devil fish do not exceed eighteen inches in length and six to eight inches in diameter when in a resting position. The animal feeds upon crabs, shrimps, and worms which it tears with the powerful beak-like jaws. The skin of the devil fish is usually brown or spotted but it has the ability to change its color to conform with that of its environment. An ink-sac may discharge a screen of ink to confuse its enemies.

The octopus has a rounded body which is marked off from the head by a neck constriction. The head bears a pair of well-developed eyes and encircling the mouth is a foot divided into eight arms. At the base the arms are connected by a web and each arm bears on its inner surface two rows of adhesive suckers. The body proper is covered by a mantle which is open in front on the ventral side. Just below the head and at the edge of the mantle is the siphon. Water is drawn into the mantle to aerate the gills and is ejected through the siphon. When the animal swims it moves backwards by expelling water rapidly through the siphon. Contrary to general belief, devil fish are timid creatures and unless trapped move stealthily out of the way of human beings.

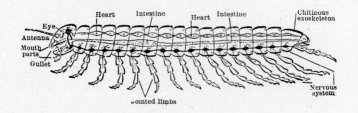

Diagrammatic representation of the structure of an
Arthropod. (From Schmeil.)

JOINTED FOOTED ANIMALS
Arthropoda

JOINTED FOOTED ANIMALS
Arthropoda

FOUR-FIFTHS of the known species of animals throughout the world are arthropods. No doubt, the reason for the vast numbers of arthropods is their successful adjustment to all environments; land, water, air, the soil, and even man himself serves as a host to parasitic forms. Arthropods include barnacles, water fleas, crabs, shrimps, lobsters, sandhoppers, insects, spiders and myriapods. Although these animals are quite unlike at first sight, they have many common characteristics. Arthropoda, meaning "jointed footed," is typical of them all. "They have bilateral symmetry, one side of the body being like the other, they are covered with a horny-like material—chitin, they are divided into segments, the segments have appendages, and the appendages are jointed so as to permit freedom of movement" (*Sea Beach at Ebb Tide*). All arthropods grow by casting off their rigid coverings and by secreting new ones. During this period of change they grow rapidly. Every hair and appendage has its special function.

Most marine arthropods are called crustaceans on account of the armour which covers their bodies; this covering ranges from a thick, limy material to a thin, transparent film. The size of crustaceans varies radically; some forms are microscopic while others may measure two feet or more in length. They live both in deep water and on the crowded littoral zone. Crustaceans are of vast economic value.

GOOSE NECK BARNACLE

Mitella polymerus

Natural size

GOOSE NECK BARNACLE
Mitella polymerus (Sowerby)

A GOOSE NECK barnacle is a strange form that differs in several respects from other sessile types. It is attached by means of a flexible leathery peduncle, three inches long. The crown, one inch across, is covered with eighteen or more plates; the plates, resembling scales, are not grown together solidly. Curled appendages protrude from between the four large plates at the top. A median, dorsal plate lies along the hinge; numerous small, irregularly arranged plates surround the base of the crown and the peduncle is covered with fine scales. The general color of the goose neck barnacle is red-brown except for the plates, which are white.

The goose neck barnacles live in crevices on rocky shores where the surf beats strongly. Frequently, they form huge masses made up of individuals of all ages and sizes.

When the larva of the goose neck barnacle settles down to a sedentary life the head region becomes attached and greatly elongated to form the peduncle.

A humorous tradition about goose neck barnacles has come down to us. In 1597, a picture appeared in an old zoology book which showed the shells of a goose neck barnacle growing on a tree with geese falling from them and swimming about in the water. Heads of little geese extended from two of the barnacles. A detailed description of this transformation accompanied the picture and ended, "But what our eyes have seen and hands have touched, we shall declare."

SMOOTH ACORN BARNACLE

Balanus crenatus

Natural size

SMOOTH ACORN BARNACLE
Balanus crenatus Bruguiere

This barnacle is extremely variable in size and shape but is probably three-fourths inch in diameter at the base and one-half inch in height. Crowded conditions and other environmental factors have much to do with the size.

In the acorn barnacle the six plates of the shell are smooth and distinct and overlap somewhat at the base. At the top the aperture is diamond shaped with the plates ending in acute points; the posterior plate folds back slightly and is curved like a beak. The calcareous shell is clear white and is almost as broad at the summit as at the base.

Another similar barnacle is *Balanus glandula* Darwin. It is a dirty white color and in crowded areas may be twice as high as it is wide. The beak seems crowded into the shell. An operculum controlled by strong muscles resembles the hooked beak of a bird.

Barnacles are hermaphroditic, male and female sex organs in the same animal. Most forms have brood pouches and carry the eggs until they hatch as free swimming larvae. Barnacles have a brain and a chain of five nerve ganglia but they have no special respiratory or circulatory organs.

Some industrious person counted the number of barnacles on a square foot of a densely colonized rock and discovered there were 2940 animals. Although barnacles can only expand and obtain food when under water they have been known to live out of water for forty-four days.

ROCK BARNACLE

Balanus cariosus

Natural size

ROCK BARNACLE
Balanus cariosus (Pallas)

BARNACLES cover the rocks on many beaches with a carpet of little, sharp-pointed pyramids. Rock barnacles vary in size from one-half inch in diameter at the base and one inch in height to one and one-half by two inches.

The body is fastened securely within the shell by strong muscles and is surrounded by a fold of skin. The thick calcareous shell, made up of six or more plates, has a porous wall and many irregular ribs with projecting points. These projecting points give the effect of a thatched roof and are produced by successive periods of growth of the animal. The shell is usually open at the top but can be closed by a four-fold door, made of two pairs of beak-like organs. When the door is closed the barnacle is safely barricaded within its home. If one listens closely, when on a barnacle strewn coast, it is possible to hear the clicks of these closing doors.

When the door is open six pairs of curled, black feather-like appendages project, forcing a current of water to the mouth. The water carries in particles of food which are masticated by the mandibles. The waving of the appendages suggests a hand regularly thrust out into the water to grasp something. Most of the body cavity is filled with the stomach.

The home and community life of barnacles must be pretty dull for they can't go places and do things. Perhaps they have a radio network to keep them informed about the doings of the barnacle world. 327

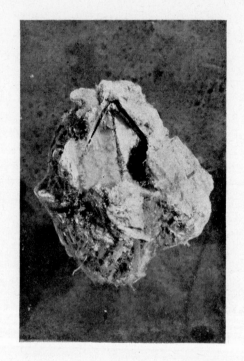

GIANT BARNACLE
Balanus nubilis

One-half natural size. Top view.

GIANT BARNACLE
Balanus nubilis Darwin

THE giant barnacle grows to be three or four inches in diameter at the base and to nearly the same height. Often a dozen or more are found in deep water growing upon one another in irregular clusters. The calcareous base and shell are thick with rough, eroded walls. This species has a large opening at the top which can be closed by a strong operculum with a pointed beak. When the animal is feeding buff colored appendages (which really are legs) project two inches or more from the beak. These sweep the water with clock-like regularity eighteen to twenty-three times a minute. Huxley has aptly said that a barnacle is a rude fellow who stands on his head and kicks food into his mouth with his heels.

Like other crustaceans, the barnacle sheds the covering of its legs, the body covering, and the lining of the shell with each moult but the protective shell itself is permanent and is enlarged as the animal grows.

A barnacle reaches sexual maturity in approximately eighty days but it is hardy and lives for several years. The larva emerges from the egg a free swimming animal but it soon settles down permanently. After attaching itself by its head it loses its shell, its eye, and swimming legs and attains its curled, feathery appendages and a new shell covering. From the time the barnacle becomes fixed until it has reached its adult form it fasts, living only by absorption of its own stored food material.

329

SAND FLEA

Orchestia traskiana

Three times natural size

SAND FLEA

Orchestia traskiana Stimpson

SAND FLEAS feed on the kelp and sea lettuce left on the beach by the outgoing tide. By lifting masses of seaweed on the beach hundreds of sand fleas may be seen jumping wildly in all directions. High jumps, hurdles, and long distance leaps are all executed with equal ease. The incoming tide drives them higher up on the beach where they dig into the sand head first and remain hidden just below the surface.

A sand flea is gray-brown or green with blue appendages. The male averages half an inch or more in length but the female is somewhat smaller. This sand flea has a laterally compressed body with gills on the thoric appendages and an elongated abdomen partially turned under. The segments of the body are not united but jointed so that the body is flexible. Three forward pairs of abdominal appendages are for swimming and the two posterior ones are used for jumping. The first thoracic appendages terminate in pincer claws. The antennae are only one-third the length of the body.

This species, or a closely related one, sews up the margins of kelp or other seaweed to make a tubular nest for itself. Thread for this needle work is secreted by glands on the first pair of appendages.

In spite of being called a "flea" this animal does not bite but is so named because of its jumping habits. Beside serving as food for fish, sand fleas are scavengers and consume large quantities of waste material.

331

SAND HOPPER

Amphithoe humeralis

Four times natural size

SAND HOPPER
Amphithoe humeralis Stimpson

THIS group of animals is not well known and the species living on the Pacific Coast have not been carefully studied. Sand hoppers are commonly seen jumping about on the sand where they feed on dead kelp or other debris. On some beaches the sand is literally covered with them.

This species of sand hopper ranges in length from one-fourth to one-half inch. Males are larger than the females and they carry the females about on the under side of their bodies for several days at the time the eggs are laid. In color, sand hoppers resemble the sand on which they live but they can take on the color of the algae or other environmental backgrounds.

The body of the sand hopper is compressed from side to side and it has an elongated abdomen. There is no hard carapace on the back but the segments are free, covered with a shiny, flexible cuticle. Gills are borne on the under side of the basal joints of the legs. Theoretically, the amphipod has the normal twenty segments of the crustacean. The first pair of antennae is long, extending more than half the length of the body; the second pair is short and stout. The eyes are not stalked. The first two pairs of thoracic appendages are modified into grasping organs, the remaining five are walking legs, three pairs directed forwards and two backwards. Three pairs of abdominal appendages are branched and are used for swimming; the last two are stiff and are used for jumping.

333

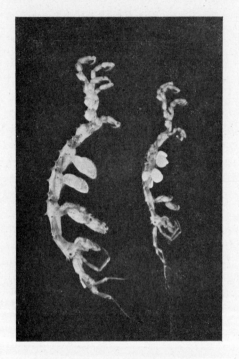

PHANTOM SHRIMP

Caprella kennerlyi

Two and one-half times natural size

PHANTOM SHRIMP
Caprella kennerlyi Stimpson

IN order to see the fragile, little *Caprella* one must examine the seaweed closely because it is almost indistinguishable from its habitat both in color and form. The grotesque phantom shrimp looks like an animated walking stick or skeleton swaying this way and that or like a measuring worm as it loops along on the sand.

This species of phantom shrimp measures from three-fourth to one inch in length and is not more than one-sixteenth inch in width; the males are somewhat larger than the females. The normal color of the smooth animal is red or yellow-brown but occasionally an almost colorless specimen is encountered. The first thoracic segment is united with the head and from the head project a pair of short forward pointed spines and two pairs of long hairy antennae. Prominent claws terminate the first and second thoracic appendages. With these claws the animal reaches out for food, bending and bowing from side to side. The last three thoracic segments are equipped with grasping organs by which it hangs on to seaweed, hydroids, or to starfish. Its habit is to stand erect and rigid awaiting chances to grasp floating organic food material. Gills are found on the third and fourth thoracic segments but there are no legs on them. Females have brood pouches situated on these segments. The abdominal segments are rudimentary, sometimes being reduced to small knobs.

GRIBBLE

Limnoria lignorum

Twenty times natural size

GRIBBLE
Limnoria lignorum (Rathke)

THE gribble is a destructive little creature that burrows with its strong jaws into wooden pilings. It can cut into wood at the rate of one-half to one inch a year, doing an enormous amount of damage. In order to secure a constant supply of fresh water a gribble does not bore deep into the wood but when it has gone in about three-fifths of an inch it comes out and begins another burrow.

A gribble is a tiny animal with a body one-eighth to one-fifth inch long divided into segments. This tiny creature has seven pairs of short legs, each ending in a sharp curved claw by means of which the animal holds on to the side of the burrow. Under the hind end of the body the appendages bear broad plates which act as gills. These keep up a continuous movement during the life of the animal and thus constantly renew the water needed for respiration.

Comparatively few young are produced and when the eggs hatch the infants begin at once to burrow near their parents. In this way the wood is honeycombed by the colony growing at the edge. The females appear to do most of the work, for though there is a pair of gribbles in each hole the female is invariably at the head end. If attacked the males crawl out of the burrow but the females stoutly resist attempts to extract them.

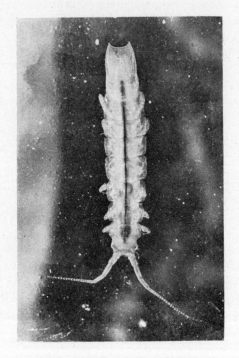

TRANSPARENT ISOPOD

Pentidotea resecata

Slightly enlarged

TRANSPARENT ISOPOD
Pentidotea resecata (Stimpson)

THIS isopod can be distinguished at once by the two sharp inward turned points on the terminal segments. The body is two inches long and one-third inch wide; the abdomen is less than one-third the entire length of the animal. Thoracic segments are broad and distinct but the abdominal segments are narrow and are often more or less fused. Legs used for walking or attachment are on the seven thoracic segments. The swimming legs fold under the abdomen and are covered ventrally by a large flap on either side. Leaf-like gills on the anterior pairs of abdominal segments serve as breathing organs. There are two pairs of antennae, one short and the other long. A dark green stripe extends down the middle of the back on the males.

The transparent isopod is a form exceedingly difficult to see for it simulates perfectly the background on which it lives. Sea lettuce and eel grass are favorite habitats and when living on them the isopod takes on an almost transparent, yellow-green color.

A female isopod takes special care of her eggs and young by carrying them in a pouch on the under side of the body. In this position they are kept constantly aereated by the paddle-like movements of the abdominal appendages. Male isopods carry the females beneath their bodies for several days during the time of sex union.

OLIVE GREEN ISOPOD
Pentidotea wosnesenskii

Two and one-half times natural size

OLIVE GREEN ISOPOD

Pentidotea wosnesenskii (Brandt)

Isopods are a widely distributed group of animals, living not only in salt water but in lakes, streams and even on land. Many species are parasitic on shrimps, crabs, and fish. A few forms are abundant on our shores hidden under rocks, on Fucus, on the big kelps or on the pilings of old wharfs. Like many other crustaceans they feed on the debris in the water. They also prey upon smaller animals and in turn are preyed upon by the larger ones. Isopods serve man indirectly by forming a part of the food for fish.

The olive green isopod is broad and flat, averaging one inch in length and one-fourth inch in width. In color, it so closely resembles the rock weed on which it lives that it is difficult to distinguish it from the background. There is a head, seven thoracic segments, and six abdominal segments. There are two pairs of antennae, one long and tapering, the other short. The eyes are compound but are not stalked. One or two of the thoracic segments are united with the head. The other thoracic segments have appendages used for locomotion; they are all similar and end in sharp points. The abdominal segments are joined into a single plate which is rounded and has a small median spine. In this species the abdominal appendages under the plate are used both for swimming and as breathing organs. These organs are protected by two lateral flaps extending the entire length of the abdomen.

341

SEA SLATER

Ligyda pallasii

Two times natural size

SEA SLATER
Ligyda pallasii (Brandt)

THIS isopod is easily distinguished by two branched, bristle-like swimmerettes on the last abdominal segment. In this species the abdominal segments are distinct and separate, the last one somewhat longer and narrower than the others. The sea slater is flat and broad, the body being nearly half as broad as long—one and one-fourth inch by one-half inch. The ground color and pattern are variable but dull gray-brown with black spots predominates; the surface is granular and the body tapers toward the posterior end. Overlapping plates which point backwards extend far beyond the sides of the body. Abdominal segments, which are not covered by flaps, contain air cavities that can be used for air breathing. Because of this adaptation this isopod prefers to stay out of the water rather than in it. It clings to the rocks above the high tide mark where it is only splashed by the waves. Here it escapes notice by remaining motionless in crevices of the rocks. Large sessile eyes are prominent on the head. One pair of antennae is inconspicuous, the other is long and jointed. Five or six pairs of appendages make up the typical, complex, crustacean mouth parts. The digestive tract is also that of a true crustacean.

The development of isopods is direct, there being no involved larval stages. The eggs and young are carried in a brood pouch, made of overlapping scales, on the under side of the female.

343

COON STRIPE SHRIMP

Pandalus danae

One-half natural size

COON STRIPE SHRIMP

Pandalus danae Stimpson

THE coon stripe shrimp gets its name from the dark red-brown transverse stripes along the sides of the body. These stripes vary in intensity and somewhat in color but are always pronounced. They may be separated by more or less irregular bands of white. While these conspicuous stripes may be used as a means of identification, the design and coloring of the back differ considerably.

The adults live in deep water but a school of young coon stripes may be seen in shallow water feeding on dead crabs or other delicious tidbits for they are voracious eaters. If disturbed they all stand at attention or suddenly dart away for they are sensitive to changes in light intensity and movements in the water. The long whip-like antennae and the constantly moving antennules both serve as sense organs.

The coon stripe shrimp is moderately strong and attains a length of five inches. The rostrum is slightly upturned; longer than the carapace, the tip is trifid, and the lower margin has six or eight spines. There are ten to twelve movable, median dorsal spines of which about half are on the carapace, but the terminal half of the rostrum has no spines above.

Several members of this genus are of commercial value. As an article of food shrimps are widely known but few of their consumers would recognize these beautiful creatures as the market product. Shrimps need to be agile for many other animals prey upon them.

GRAY OR ALASKA SHRIMP

Crago alaskensis

Natural size

GRAY OR ALASKA SHRIMP
Crago alaskensis (Rathbun)

THE gray shrimp can be recognized by the large pincer claws on the first pair of walking legs. These claws form a sort of hand, two and one-half to three times as long as is broad, with a thumb ending in a spine and a finger folding against the margin of the hand. A small median spine is on the short rostrum. Long, delicate feelers serve as sense organs. The stalked eyes are small and are of nearly the same color as the body. A peculiar sandy effect in the coloration of the animal makes it hard to see when at the bottom of a pool. Considerable blue-green iridescence shows along the edges of the thoracic segments and on the walking legs. A gray shrimp grows to be two inches long with a carapace one-half inch in length.

As is the habit of all shrimps the female gray shrimp carries the eggs attached to the swimmer-ettes, or abdominal appendages, on the under side of the body. The eggs hatch in about two months but shrimps do not spawn until they are two years old.

Shrimps walk forward by using the thoracic appendages and swim backwards by means of the abdominal appendages. They are agile creatures, which, aided by their protective coloring, are usually successful in escaping their enemies. The long antennae warn them of approaching danger. Shrimps are so delicious that they are the prey of countless fish and other carniverous animals. Shrimps can regenerate lost limbs.

347

SHORT SPINE SHRIMP
Spirontocaris brevirostris

Slightly enlarged

SHORT SPINE SHRIMP
Spirontocaris brevirostris Dana

THE short spine shrimp is found all the way from Alaska to San Francisco Bay, where it appears both in shallow water and in deep water down to about 150 feet. It is more common in the north. This shrimp is stout but is seldom more than one and one-half inches in length and is consequently too small to be of commercial value. Many of this genus are much smaller than this species. The rostrum is short, reaching little if any beyond the cornea. There are five or six median dorsal spines of which the last three or four are on the carapace and the lower margin of the rostrum is unarmed. The color is usually quite bright but the shrimp simulates the hues of its background successfully.

Shrimps carry their eggs until they hatch attached to abdominal appendages called the pleopoda. The young pass through a metamorphosis in many respects quite as remarkable as the change from a caterpillar into a butterfly. Before emerging from the egg they may have passed through several larval stages and still look so little like their parents that they have in some cases been given other names for a time. The larva of a short spined shrimp is only one and five-tenths millimeters long when hatched and has no rostrum. Hundreds are hatched but only a few survive for they are apt to become the food of many larger animals.

"One touch of nature makes the whole world kin."
—Shakespeare.

MARINE CRAYFISH
Upogebia pugettensis

Two-thirds natural size

MARINE CRAYFISH
Upogebia pugettensis Dana

At about mean low tide on many gravelly or muddy beaches, where there are sea lettuce and decayed vegetation, the burrowing marine crayfish live concealed in subterranean passageways. Except for the openings to the burrows and the mounds thrown up in the process of excavation one might never suspect their presence. With their summits somewhat depressed, the mounds look like the cinder cones of miniature volcanoes. To explore these burrows requires plenty of patience and a stout shovel for they sometimes extend to a depth of three feet. In general, the burrows are nearly vertical and Y-shaped. In excavating, the crayfish scoops out the load by using the outer foot jaws. The sand is loaded into a sort of basket formed by the outstretched chelipeds for sides and the first pair of walking legs with long interlaced hairs for a very effective bottom.

The marine crayfish may have a muddy tan appearance but when washed is found to be buff mottled with deep olive or blue. The rostrum is short and broad and has a stubble of short hairs which partly conceal the cylindrical eye stalks. The chelipeds are equal in size and the outer foot jaws are much like walking legs.

While the marine crayfish do not prey upon oysters they bring about their destruction by smothering them and by breaking the dykes built around the oyster beds.

GHOST SHRIMP

Callianassa gigas

Natural size

GHOST SHRIMP
Callianassa gigas Dana

A GHOST shrimp is a strange animal, living in a tube, which has a smooth, glossy, white membranous covering through which the dark internal organs can be plainly seen. The animal is about five inches long and one inch wide. The Y- or U-shaped burrows of the ghost shrimp are made of sand and fine gravel and extend to a depth of two or three feet. At the opening of the burrow is a mound of gravel. Although the tube is scarcely wider than the animal it can turn around in the tube by rolling its abdomen under itself and executing a somersault. Digging is done by the complex mouth parts and the load is carried out by the claws and walking legs. A big load is about one teaspoonful.

The claws are extremely unequal in size. The second pair of walking legs is also developed into claws. When in motion the ghost shrimp usually bends the large claw so it is about the same size as the smaller one which is extended straight ahead, but sometimes it travels with this cumbersome appendage fully extended. The pads of hairs on the last two pairs of walking legs serve as brushes in keeping the body clean and well groomed. The elongated abdomen has appendages adapted for swimming and ends in a broad tail fin.

There is a short rostrum and blunt eye stalks. Antennae, half as long as body, extend from the front of the animal and the antennules are half as long as the antennae.

HAIRY HERMIT CRAB
Pagurus hirsutiusculus

Natural size

HAIRY HERMIT CRAB
Pagurus hirsutiusculus (Dana)

MANY humorous blunders have crept into the nomenclature of animals and the name "hermit crab" is one of these, for the hermit crab is neither a hermit nor a crab. He is a most sociable fellow and his structure is quite unlike that of a crab.

A hermit crab does not have a hard covering on the posterior part of the body and therefore he seeks protection by inserting his soft abdomen into a hollow object, usually a snail shell. All the abdominal segments are more or less undeveloped and degenerate but the sixth segment has developed hooks and with these the animal fastens itself to the spiral of the shell.

The hermit crab is decidedly hairy, especially on the walking legs. Variations in color from bright blue to olive appear on the thorax. The claws are a dull gray with bright blue granules, the fingers are white above and blue below, and the walking legs are white or blue. The long antennae are brown with yellow spots. The first pair of walking legs is enlarged into powerful pincer claws, the one on the right is larger and more powerful than the one on the left. Besides the usual function of capturing and crushing prey the right hand serves as a door to close the mouth of the shell; the small left hand completes the closing. The second and third pairs of walking legs are well developed but the fourth and fifth pairs are much reduced.

BERING HERMIT CRAB

Pagurus beringanus

Slightly enlarged

BERING HERMIT CRAB
Pagurus beringanus (Benedict)

THIS hermit crab is common on rocky beaches and in tide pools where it walks about with its house on its back. The animal is brussels brown in color with brighter markings. The claws have scarlet spines and the fingers are a pale green tipped with scarlet. Two pairs of highly developed walking legs are green marked with large, irregular spots of red on the joints. Long, flexible antennae are also a bright brown, ringed with white. Almost the whole dorsal surface of the body and the walking legs are covered with hairs. The pincer claws are somewhat unequal in size; both are covered with spines and coarse granules.

Constant grooming is necessary for a hermit crab. Using either claw with equal ease it rubs and scrapes all parts of the fore body, appendages, eye stalks, and feelers. Were the crab to neglect these toilet duties the rough body covering would soon be overgrown with foreign material. Old crabs often become careless in this respect and are soon covered with debris. Considerable house cleaning is necessary before a shell is sufficiently sanitary for a hermit crab to occupy and the prospective occupant carefully carries out the waste and rubbish that have accumulated within. Hermit crabs are scavengers and do much toward keeping the beaches clean. Hermit crabs like to fight, and three or four may engage in a free-for-all tussle.

THIN HAND HERMIT CRAB

Pagurus tenuimanus

Natural size

THIN HAND HERMIT CRAB
Pagurus tenuimanus (Dana)

THE thin hand hermit crab is a common variety found all the way from the beach to deep water. Its brilliant coloring and the extreme unequal size of the claws make it a species easy to identify. The small hand is hardly more than one-fourth as wide as the large one. The carapace shades from cinnamon to brown, with orange and blue markings; appendages vary from brown to blue with longitudinal maroon stripes and spots. The large claws are cinnamon colored with white spots. Long, stout eye stalks project far beyond the head and the ringed antennae are long and firm.

When the animal is removed from its shell, one sees that the carapace is smooth and of nearly equal length and breadth. The abdominal appendages are much degenerate but definite hooks for attachment to the shell take the place of the sixth pair. Covering the abdomen is a thin skin so delicate that the slightest abrasion will rupture it. To protect this delicate abdomen the hermit crab covers it with a shell and if it changes its domicile it does so with the utmost speed to avoid being seized by an enemy. The only reason for leaving its house is that the animal molts several times a year and during this period grows rapidly and must move to larger quarters to accommodate the increased size. If the hermit crab survives the perils of these journeys it may live for four years.

TUFT-HAIRED CRAB

Hapalogaster mertensii

Natural size

TUFT-HAIRED CRAB
Hapalogaster mertensii Brandt

THIS CRAB is recognized at once by the long spines and other projections that completely cover the heart-shaped carapace and the legs. It is also distinguished by the fact that the fifth pair of legs, which is rudimentary, is folded under the carapace within the gill chamber, so that the crab appears to have but four legs on each side. An average sized specimen has a carapace about an inch in length and is nearly the same width. The chelipeds, or pincer claws, are not much longer than the walking legs and both are flattened. Two long, banded antennae are situated inside of the stalked eyes. They are equipped with senses of touch and smell and wave and move in all directions.

A peculiar characteristic of the tuft-haired crab is the soft, sac-like abdomen that does not fit completely under the thorax, and for that reason it is easily injured. On the upper surface the crab is a dull, drab color on account of the sand and dirt that adhere to the spines and hairs. Below, the body and legs are bare and red. It is a species exceedingly difficult to distinguish from its surroundings.

Mouth parts of crabs are complex and variable, but there is generally a pair of short, hard mandibles, which work from side to side. Outside of these are the short maxillae and the long maxillipeds, which assist in holding and manipulating the food.

PORCELAIN CRAB
Petrolisthes eriomerus

Natural size

PORCELAIN CRAB
Petrolisthes eriomerus Stimpson

THE PORCELAIN CRAB is characterized by the extreme flatness of the carapace and the enormous sharp claws which extend far beyond the carapace. It has a small nearly circular carapace one-half to three-fourths inch in diameter. Long whip-like antennae, often three times as long as the carapace, move about constantly. Three pairs of walking legs are uniform in size and are somewhat hairy; the last pair is small and rudimentary and folds over the base of the carapace.

In general, the color of the porcelain crab is brown with flecks of bright blue. The claws are brown or blue and the walking legs are marked with gray stripes. This crab, found at extreme low tide mark, heightens its resemblance to the rocks under which it lives by fringing the tiny hairs on the limbs and carapace with mud and sand.

A hard covering of lime forms a shell on the back and legs of a crab. This covering has little spaces at the joints to give some freedom of movement but any increase in size is impossible with such an unwieldy covering, so it is shed periodically. The animal is able to loosen its covering while forming a new one below. Finally, the crab emerges from the old covering through a slit between the carapace and the abdomen. The crab is now soft and tender and is capable of great growth in the few days before the new shell hardens. When people speak of soft shell crabs they refer to this period of transition.

PURPLE SHORE CRAB

Hemigrapsus nudus

Natural size

PURPLE SHORE CRAB
Hemigrapsus nudus (Dana)

A visitor to the sea shore sees the purple shore crab if everything else escapes his notice. This crab is omnipresent, scurrying among the rocks, running over the sand or intent upon devouring dead fish. It prefers a rocky shore to a sandy beach, and every rock probably harbors half a dozen crabs. This crab can remain out of water for a considerable time, and crawls far up on the beach.

The carapace—the hard covering of the back— is smooth and almost square, averaging one to one and one-half inches in length and width. The corners of the carapace are rounded, those in front are deeply notched and from the notches the stalked eyes project, while the posterior corners are concave, making a place of attachment for the last pair of legs. Color and markings vary considerably—yellow-green, red-brown, and purple specimens appear together but the purple tinge seems to predominate. Red-purple spots are usually present on the claws, and the carapace is decidedly mottled. The underside of the crab is nearly white. As the scientific name implies, this is a nude species without spines or hairs of any kind on the surface. In common with most crustaceans, the first pair of walking legs has developed into strong pincers. The other four pairs of walking legs are of nearly equal size and end in single sharp claws.

GRACEFUL KELP CRAB

Pugettia gracilis

One-half natural size

GRACEFUL KELP CRAB
Pugettia gracilis Dana

THIS shy little crab ornaments itself with sea-weed, sponge or bryozoa which it attaches to stiff hairs on the carapace. The decorations are fastened on by the crab itself which uses the slender legs for this purpose. This masking is important for both offensive and defensive purposes. When these trappings are stripped off one finds that the carapace is triangular in shape, the rostrum being formed by two diverging prongs. Several sharp points project from the upper edges of the carapace. The claws are long and narrow with the fingers shorter than the palms. The four pairs of walking legs are of nearly equal size and length.

A large specimen may measure two and one-half inches in length and one and one-half inches in width. On the dorsal surface the graceful kelp crab is usually green; on the ventral side it is a light yellow or tan. A few red specimens are found.

In most species of crabs the eggs remain attached to the female by the numerous hairs on the swimmerettes until time for hatching. While the crab is carrying the eggs the abdominal segments are not held close to the body but extend out half an inch or more. In this position the eggs are kept supplied with oxygen by the paddle-like movements of the swimmerettes. When hatched the young larvae emerge as forms so different from the parents that for a long time they were considered entirely distinct animals.

NORTHERN KELP CRAB

Pugettia (Epialtus) productus

One-half natural size

NORTHERN KELP CRAB
Pugettia (Epialtus) productus Randall

YOUNG kelp crabs are found in tide pools and on the eel grass but older specimens are usually in the kelp off shore. The carapace of the kelp crab is perfectly smooth and except for the rostrum is more or less rectangular in shape with two distinct points on each side. The rostrum is divided into two sharp points or horns. The pincer claws are large and powerful but are shorter than the first pair of walking legs. All four pairs of walking legs are long and smooth and stouter than those of most spider crabs. The color of the dorsal surface is dull olive, mottled with spots of a darker shade; the ventral surface is light tan and the mouth parts and claws may be marked with bright red. An average sized kelp crab measures two and one-half inches in width from tip to tip of the lateral teeth and three inches in length.

Some of the finest cases of protective resemblance known occur in the crabs. Kelp crabs which live on the large brown kelps or among dull, green rock weeds resemble these plants closely. Some crabs decorate themselves with foreign material; some have rough hairs and spines; some have carapaces flattened like ordinary pebbles and long claws suggestive of old worm tubes; some crabs resemble discarded bivalve shells; and others make themselves inconspicuous by entangling the hairs on the edges of the carapaces with mud and dirt so that the bodies grade off into the surrounding rocks.

LYRE CRAB

Hyas lyratus

One-half natural size

LYRE CRAB
Hyas lyratus Dana

The lyre crab receives its name from the lyre-like shape of its carapace which measures up to two inches in length and one and one-half inches in width. A lyre crab conceals itself from its enemies by a skillful art of camouflage. It gathers seaweed, hydroids, sponges and small shells with its long pincers and places them on its back. If a crab is near a bed of green algae the decorations will be green seaweed, if among hydroids the masking will be hydroids. In other words the dress is changed with reference to the fauna and flora of the locality. The animal accomplishes this by placing the material in its mouth where it is moistened by a secretion of mucous and then cemented to its back. Hairs and rough projections on the back aid in holding the foreign materials in place.

The lyre crab has a thick, round body narrowing in front to a long beak-like projection which ends in two hooked prongs. It has long slender legs which are active and somewhat flexible. There are small calcareous knobs at the base of the antennae and a projection just behind the eyes formed by the union of two spines. The carapace is usually a gray or tan color but it is frequently marked with red spots and the legs have red or gray bands.

BLACK-CLAWED CRAB

Lophopanopeus bellus

Slightly enlarged

BLACK-CLAWED CRAB
Lophopanopeus bellus (Stimpson)

THE carapace of an average sized black-clawed crab measures three-fourths inch in length and is one and one-fourth inches in width at the anterior portion but it is narrower toward the back. The carapace is convex with a notch in the center front and two prominent notches just behind the widest point of the shell. It is flattened at the back. There are irregular grooves on the back which give the appearance of a network. The rounded claws are strong and powerful; the walking legs are small and thin.

Coloration varies greatly in this species but the anterior part of the carapace is frequently red-brown or purple and the posterior part gray. The legs are colored the same as the carapace but with heavy gray spots. Occasionally the claws are white but they are always tipped with black. The under side of the crab is much lighter than the upper side. This crab is found buried in sand or mud on rocky shores.

All crabs move sideways using the legs on one side for pulling and those on the other for pushing. The legs do not all move at the same time so a continuous and uniform motion is kept up. As a rule shore crabs lie in wait for their prey and aided by their keen senses of sight and smell artfully grab the victims when they approach.

EDIBLE CRAB

Cancer magister

One-fourth natural size

EDIBLE CRAB
Cancer magister Dana

THE common edible crab of the Pacific Coast is *Cancer magister*. It attains a breadth of seven to nine inches. It occurs most commonly on sandy bottoms below low tide but is often seen about wharfs and piers. The upper surface is light red-brown, darkest in front and the limbs and under surface are yellow. The front of the carapace has five unequal teeth but they do not protrude beyond the other parts. The surface of the carapace is slightly convex, covered with very fine bumps and the teeth of its saw-like margins are spine tipped.

These heavy crabs are very clumsy on land but in shallow water they move lightly along over the sandy bottom on the tips of their legs. Much of their time is spent almost entirely buried in the sand, and thus to free the water entering the gills from sediment is a vital problem. The coarser particles are strained out as the water passes through the space between the toothed margins of the shell and the large pincers folded against the sides of the body. A very dense coat of hairs on the under side removes the finer particles. By occasionally reversing the current this strainer is kept efficient.

Cancer magister is sold as a hard crab. At the time of molting the flesh of this crab undergoes changes that make it undesirable for food.

RED CANCER CRAB
Cancer productus

One and one-half times natural size

RED CANCER CRAB
Cancer productus Randall

THE red crab, *Cancer productus*, is rather numerous at low tide on gravelly shores where there is little or no mud. It is also found along rocky shores beneath the stones and may live at a depth of several fathoms. Nevertheless, though similar in many respects to *C. magister* (see previous page) this crab is more restricted in habit for it has no provision for straining muddy water such as is possessed by *C. magister*. Most adults are dark red above and lighter below. The young sometimes look like the adults but they may be practically white, striped, streaked or mottled to such an extent that they are often mistaken for a different species. However, they are readily distinguished from other cancer crabs by the front of the carapace—which has five equal scallops between the eyes and which extends forward more than the other parts. The surface of the carapace is nearly smooth and its antero-lateral margins are sawlike but not spine tipped as in *C. magister*. The dactyls (movable fingers) of the large claws are black on the inner margins nearly to the joint and are darkened from the tip about half this distance on the outer margin.

Cancer productus sometimes measures five to seven inches in breadth, and is found from Alaska to California. It is edible but is not abundant enough to be used commercially. There are nine species of cancer crabs found on the Pacific Coast.

HAIRY CANCER CRAB

Cancer oregonensis

One and one-half times natural size

HAIRY CANCER CRAB
Cancer oregonensis (Dana)

THE hairy cancer crab is smaller than the other members of the genus, having a carapace two-thirds inch long and one inch wide. It may be distinguished by its nearly circular carapace with twelve or thirteen distinct, granulated notches along the margin. The surface of the carapace is irregular with numerous bumps and deep depressions which give the crab an untidy appearance. Around the carapace is a fringe of hairs and the legs are hairy. The antennae are short and the eyes are large and stalked. Claws with dark fingers are of equal size. Irregular white spots tend to give the legs a somewhat banded appearance. The color of the hairy cancer crab is dark red above and much lighter below. This crab is found abundantly at extreme low tide buried in mud and fine sand under rocks and in shallow water. Hairy crabs are too small to be used commercially.

Crabs (like human beings) are said to get the "wanderlust" and go traveling each autumn. In September, adult crabs begin to move outward from the shore to deeper water, going to a depth of 150 to 200 feet. They remain in deep water until February and while there the females spawn. By that time they are eager to return home and by May the majority of the crabs are close to shore again. The females carry the eggs on the abdominal segments during the return journey and in the warm inshore waters the larvae are hatched. In the following autumn the migration begins again.

BRISTLY OR HORSE CRAB

Telmessus cheiragonus

Two-thirds natural size

BRISTLY OR HORSE CRAB
Telmessus cheiragonus (Tilesius)

THIS crab seems to be limited to the waters of Puget Sound for it is unreported elsewhere. The carapace and equal walking legs are covered with bristle-like scales and stiff hairs arranged in irregular rows. Color variations are from a yellow-brown to a dark brown. Six large projections on each side of the carapace and three on the front give a saw-tooth effect to the margin. One writer describes the shape as helmet-like or pentagonal. The extreme width from the long fourth projection is one and one-half inches and the length is one and one-fourth inches. A deep depression is noticeable in the center front of the carapace and the entire surface is roughened.

Crabs are scavengers, feeding on whatever material they can find. A crab seizes its food with the powerful pincer claws and by these it is crushed and pushed into the mouth. Here the food is torn and shredded by the jaws until it is fine enough to be swallowed. The stomach of the crab is lined with a horny material and a set of three tooth-like structures in the stomach grind the food until it is very fine. It is then strained through fine hairs. Two glands, sometimes called livers, situated at the sides of the stomach, secrete a fluid into the intestine to aid in digestion. The digestive tract is surrounded by a cavity filled with blood which absorbs the products of digestion. An anal opening terminates the digestive tract.

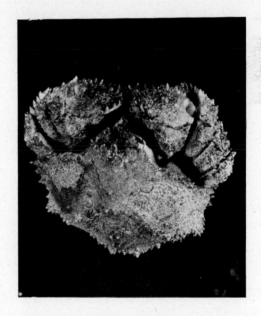

BOX CRAB

Lopholithodes foraminatus

One-third natural size

BOX CRAB
Lopholithodes foraminatus (Stimpson)

THE largest and most colorful crab of this region is the box crab which measures about eight inches in width and six inches in length. Its color is a brilliant scarlet or orange with bright, purple markings on the under side of the body and on the spines on the legs. The most prominent feature of this crab is the large, circular opening between the claws and the first pair of walking legs. This hole permits the passage of water over the gills when the legs are folded in front of the carapace. The entire surface of the crab is covered with large projections and tubercles. The claws are short and stout and have many spines. All the walking legs are covered with large projections except the last pair, which is rudimentary and folded under the gills. One large prong and two lateral spines form the rostrum, and the eyes are covered with spines.

This crab is not a shore form except when there are unusually low tides. It may also be found on the beach when it has shed its old covering and a new one is being formed beneath. At this time the crab tries to hide itself, for thus undressed it is a prey of hungry enemies. During this period of change a crab is often called a soft-shelled crab.

There is a similar species *(Lopholithodes mandtii)*, the king crab, which is without the opening between the claws and first pair of walking legs.

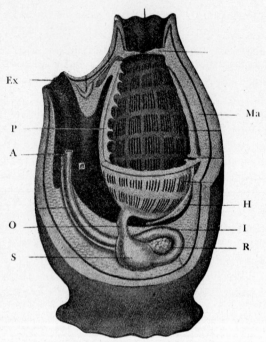

(Adapted from Hegner)

VERTEBRATE ANIMALS
Phylum Chordata

Diagram of a tunicate.
M. inhalant siphon and mouth; Ma. mantle; H. heart; I. Intestine; R. reproductive organ; S. stomach; O. oesophagus; A. anus; P. pharynx; Ex. exhalant siphon.

VERTEBRATE ANIMALS
Phylum Chordata

ALL THE higher animals from tunicates to mammals, including man, belong to the Phylum Chordata or vertebrate animals. This group has a notochord, an elastic rod-like support of the body either in the embryonic or the adult stage. In certain low chordates the notochord remains through life, but in higher forms it is replaced by a bony spinal column. A second feature which disinguishes the chordates is the central, tubular nervous system which lies back of the notochord. A third distinctive feature of the chordates is the presence of gill slits. These gill slits function throughout life in most of the lower chordates but in the higher air breathing forms the gill clefts are present only in the embryonic stages. Respiration is carried on by means of lungs in the air breathing animals.

A study of the chordates should not be included in a survey of invertebrate seashore animals but there is one group, the tunicates, that are on the border line between the vertebrates and invertebrates. The tunicate has a notochord in the larval stage but this disappears in the adult form and the animal is considered degenerate. Tunicates are especially interesting because of the remarkable changes they undergo in their life histories. Tunicates receive their name from the tunic, a covering of cellulose tisue, that envelopes the body. They are also called sea-squirts.

GLASSY SEA SQUIRT
Ascidiopsis paratropa

Two-thirds natural size

GLASSY SEA SQUIRT
Ascidiopsis paratropa Huntsman

THIS species of tunicate is easily recognized by the transparent body covering through which the internal organs can be seen. It is a cylindrical bag-like animal tapering slightly at each end and is attached to a rock or shell by a small irregular area at the lower end. Many large, irregular tubercles cover the surface of the tunicate. Two siphon openings are on the upper end; the one which carries off the water stands higher than the one controlling the incoming current. A glassy tunicate may reach a length of four inches but is usually somewhat shorter and has a width and thickness of approximately two inches.

A rather highly organized arrangement of the internal organs is present. The stomach and the looped intestine occupy a large part of the body cavity. Simple tunicates reproduce sexually with both sexual products occurring in the same animal.

Tunicates, or sea squirts, as they are generally called, are practically unknown to many people who visit the seashore. They are shapeless, unattractive creatures often mistaken for stones, seaweed or sponges. Even when they squirt forth water one is apt to think it was ejected by a nearby clam. Sea squirts are probably the dullest and most degenerate of any animals found on the beach.

Sea squirts live only one year and may even go through several generations in one summer.

PEANUT SEA· SQUIRT

Styela gibbsii

One and one-half times natural size

PEANUT SEA SQUIRT
Styela gibbsii (Stimpson)

A PEANUT sea squirt is a cylindrical animal attached at the posterior end by a short stalk. A good sized specimen measures from one to two inches in length and one-half inch in diameter and is yellow-brown in color, becoming red toward the tips of the siphons. The surface is slightly roughened by circular ridges and longitudinal folds. Sand grains adhere to hairy processes at the posterior end of the tunic. Many peanut sea squirts grow together in dense clusters. The siphons are short but distinct; the branchial siphon has a downward curve and the excurrent opening is upright.

The outside covering of a tunicate is made of a stout, gristly translucent or transparent layer called the tunic. This covering, or exoskeleton, contains much cellulose, a substance not often found in animals but entering largely into the composition of plants. This skeleton is pierced only by the two siphon openings. The mantle, attached firmly only at the siphon openings, is suspended freely within the tunic.

For want of a bettter nomenclature the name of a number of our common vegetables and fruits have been given to the seashore animals. In the sea are found sea lemons, sea peaches, sea strawberries, sea walnuts, sea peanuts, sea corn, sea oats, sea cucumbers, and sea gherkins. And strange and incongruous as it is, all these so-called vegetables and fruits are animals.

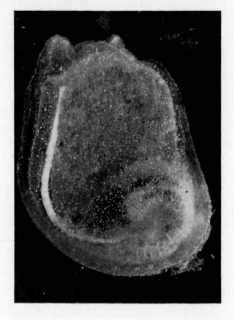

INFLATED TRANSPARENT SEA SQUIRT

Corella inflata

Two times natural size

INFLATED TRANSPARENT SEA SQUIRT
Corella inflata Huntsman

THE BODY covering of this sea squirt is perfectly smooth and transparent, so it has no secrets from the eyes of the world about its internal anatomy. The body is short and nearly square, one and one-half inches in length and breadth, and it is much swollen by an enlargement of the excurrent chamber. Two short siphons project at the top of the animal. This sea squirt is attached by a small area at the posterior end.

This is an excellent species in which to study the arrangement of the organs of the alimentary canal and the circulation of the transparent blood. One sees a heavy, white, tubular gonad running along the intestine and the network of chambers in the branchial sac through which the blood flows. A peculiar feature of the tunicates is the blood vascular system and the pulsations of the sac-shaped heart. The heart is a tubular organ near the lower end of the transparent body. With the aid of a microscope "the beating" of the heart as a succession of rhythmic waves passing in one direction from one end of the organ to the other is noticed. Then the beats gradually grow slower until they cease altogether for a few seconds. At the end of this short interval of rest, the pulsations begin again from the opposite direction. The beats become gradually stronger until another rest period is reached and then once more there is a reversal in the course of the pulsations.

HORSESHOE SEA SQUIRT

Chelyosoma productum

Natural size

HORSESHOE SEA SQUIRT
Chelyosoma productum (Stimpson)

THE HORSESHOE squirt is attached by the right side, stands about an inch in height, is an inch in diameter and has the upper surface flattened to form a disk. The outer covering of the animal is a translucent, tough material covered with plates. On the upper surface are two short, inconspicuous siphons each surrounded by six triangular lobes. When the tunicate is undisturbed water flows through the siphons in a steady stream so that the branchial sac is always filled with water. If the animal is irritated it quickly contracts the muscles of the body wall and ejects jets of water through the siphon openings.

A tunicate has a large pharynx into which the mouth opens. This organ also serves for respiration for it is perforated by gill slits which form a complicated network. Many blood vessels pass through the network and the blood is well supplied with oxygen by a current of water constantly flowing through the pharynx. The water brings in tiny animals and plants to be used as food materials. By means of cilia the food is directed through the pharynx to the oesophagus, the stomach, the looped intestine and finally the waste materials are carried off through the excurrent siphon. The digested food is absorbed by the wall of the alimentary canal and is carried by the blood to the body tissues.

Tunicates are called sea squirts because when touched they send out jets of water.

BROAD BASE SEA SQUIRT

Cnemidocarpa joanne

Natural size

BROAD BASE SEA SQUIRT
Cnemidocarpa joanne (Herdman)

THIS sea squirt has a low, rounded body which is attached over an extensive area and varies in shape depending upon the kind of surface to which the animal adheres. At the base it covers an area of one to two square inches and the height is about half as great as the base. Frequently, this sea squirt is found among a cluster of other species, but its bright orange color and perfectly smooth surface make it a conspicuous form. The siphons are placed far apart and stand up like two short tubes. The body covering is a tough, rubbery material that readily splits into layers. Tube worms, algae and hybrids often grow around the base in untidy profusion.

The nervous system of an adult tunicate consists of a single ganglion which breaks up into fibers that go to different parts of the body, especially to the lobes and muscles around the siphons. In the outer tunic or skin are sensory cells but the animal is poorly provided with definite sense organs. The tentacles are not efficient organs of touch for they are some distance within the siphons. Apparently, the most sensitive parts of the body are the expanded margins of the siphons. There is a curiously curled projection near the entrance of the branchial sac that may be an organ for testing by smell or taste the quality of the water to be drawn into the siphon.

HAIRY SEA SQUIRT

Boltenia villosa

Two   times natural size

HAIRY SEA SQUIRT
Boltenia villosa (Stimpson)

THE hairy sea squirt is a form quite irregular in size and shape. It may have a rounded or oblong body about an inch in length and width that is attached by a stalked base. The stalk is sometimes extremely short and sometimes three or four times as long as the body. On the hard rough surface of the sea squirt are numerous flexible simple or branched spines to which great quantities of foreign material may adhere. When these hydroids, algae, shells and mud are removed one sees that the body covering is a yellow-tan color and the short siphons shade from orange to a deep red. The siphons are short and distinct from one another; water enters the body through the curved siphon and passes from it through the straight one.

Tunicates were not recognized as chordates until the development of the eggs and the metamorphosis of the larvae were fully studied. It was then learned that the typical larvae, which is about one-eighth inch long and resembles a frog tadpole, has a distinct notochord, a neural tube and pharyngeal gills. This little larva is free swimming and propels itself forward by lateral strokes of the tail. After a few days as a free swimming form the larva secretes a sticky fluid and becomes attached to a solid object. It then loses all means of locomotion, the notochord and the neural tube, undergoes a definite degeneration, and becomes an adult tunicate.

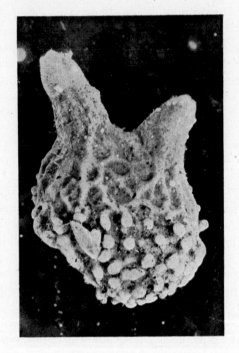

WARTY SEA SQUIRT

Pyura haustor

One and one-half times natural size

WARTY SEA SQUIRT
Pyura haustor Stimpson

THE warty sea squirt is distinguished by its prominent, red tipped siphons and the exceedingly rough, warty, gray or brown surface. This warty appearance is produced by a network of coarse ridges from which tubercles arise. The siphons are some distance apart; the longer one receives the water and the shorter one expels it. In the siphons is an external layer of circular fibers and an internal layer of longitudinal fibers which control the intake and outlet of the water. The species is so variable in size and shape that it is difficult to give measurements but an average animal may be one and one-half inches in length and nearly the same diameter with siphons one-half to three-fourths inch long. Frequently, warty sea squirts grow in irregular masses and are so covered with tube worms, hydroids, algae and sand that only the siphons are visible.

Tunicates all live in the sea and occur at varying depths although the greater number have the shore for their habitat. They range in size from a hundredth of an inch to more than one foot in diameter. Some of the tropical forms are brilliantly colored but the vivid coloring does not appear to be of any particular value to its owner. Thirteen hundred species of tunicates have been described. Tunicates have been known since the time of Aristotle but it was not until the middle of the nineteenth century that they were accurately described. The relationship of tunicates and chordates was not demonstrated before the middle of that century.

COMPOUND SEA SQUIRT

Amaroucium californicum

One-half natural size

COMPOUND SEA SQUIRT
Amaroucium californicum Ritter and Forsyth

COMPOUND tunicates are colonies in which the individual members of the group are joined by a common tunic. They also possess a common cloaca, a sac-like space which receives the discharges of the various organs. The original member of the colony is produced sexually but the colony grows by a system of budding.

This species usually forms a massive, hemispherical colony five to six inches in diameter, which is slightly cartilaginous in consistency. It adheres closely to stones in shallow water or is exposed at extreme low tide. The colony ranges in color from an opalescent white to red-brown or purple. The mass is often divided into lobed clusters, called systems, standing on short stalks. Individual zooids of this species are clearly visible as small dots on the surface. Each zooid carries on its own independent life and has an elongated body, perpendicular to the surface of the colony. It is composed of three regions, thorax, abdomen and post-abdomen. Budding takes place by a division of the post-abdominal region which contains the gonads and the heart.

Compound tunicates may be confused with sponges for they are of much the same size, shape, and color, but the compound tunicates contract somewhat when touched, force water from their openings and are composed of a gelatinous or cartilaginous material. There are many genera and species of compound tunicates but only one form is common on our shores.

BIBLIOGRAPHY

Agersborg, H. P. K.—*Notes on Melibe Leonina* (Gould). *Pub.* Puget Sound Biol. Station, Vol. 2, 1919.

Agersborg, H. P. K.—*Gymnosomatous Pteropoda from Friday Harbor, Washington*. Ann. Sci. Nat. et Zool. 10 series, Vol. 6, 1923.

Arnold, Augusta Foot—*The Sea Beach at Ebb Tide*. Century Co., N. Y., 1901.

Beebe, William—*Arcturus Adventure*. G. P. Putnam's Sons. N. Y., N. Y., 1926.

Burgess, Thornton W.—*The Burgess Sea Shore Book for Children*. Little, Brown and Co., Boston, 1929.

Bush, Mildred—*Revised Key to the Echinoderms of Friday Harbor, Washington*. Pub. Puget Sound Biol. Sta. Vol. 3, 1921.

Coe, W. P.—*Harriman Alaska Expedition,* Vol. XI. Nemerteans of the Expedition. Doubleday, Page and Co., 1904.

Cooke, A. H.—*Cambridge Natural History*, Vol. 3, Molluscs. Macmillan and Co., Ltd., London, 1913.

Cornwall, Ira E.—*Review of Crepidula of Coast of British Columbia*. Contr. to Canadian Biology, N. S. Vol. 2, 1925.

Creswell, E. J. J.—*Sponges, Their Nature, History, Modes of Fishing, etc.* Pitman, N. Y., 1922.

Crowder, William—*Between the Tides*. Dodd, Mead, and Co., N. Y., 1931.

Crowder, William—*Dwellers of the Sea and Shore*. Macmillan Co., N. Y., 1923.

Duncan, F. M.—*Animals of the Sea*. Nelson, N. Y., 1924.

Flatterly and Walton—*The Biology of the Sea Shore*. Macmillan and Co., N. Y., 1922.

Fraser, C. McLean—*A Comparison of the Marine Fauna of the Nanaimo Region with that of the San Juan Archipelago*. Trans. Roy. Soc. Canada, Vol. 26, Section 5, 1932.

Figuier, L. G.—*Ocean World*. Cassell, London, 1872.

Freeman Daniel—*The Polyclads of the San Juan Region of Puget Sound*. Trans. Amer. Microscopical Soc., Vol. 52, 1933.

Hegner, Robert—*College Zoology*, Macmillan and Co., N. Y., 1932.

Hegner, Robert—*Invertebrate Zoology*. Macmillan and Co., N. Y. 1933.

Hegner, Robert—*Parade of the Animal Kingdom*. Macmillan and Co., New York, 1935.

Herdman, W. A.—*Ascidia*. Liverpool Marine Biology Committee Memoir, I. T. Dobb and Co., Liverpool, 1899.

Huntsman, A. G.—*Holosomateus Ascidians from the Coast of Western Canada*. Contr. to Canadian biology, No. 10, 1906-10.

Johnson and Snook—*Seashore Animals of the Pacific Coast*. Macmillan and Co., N. Y., 1927.

Johnson, Herbert Parlin—*The Polychaeta of the Puget Sound Region*. Proc. Boston Soc. of Nat. Hist., Vol. 29, 1901.

Keep, Josiah—*West Coast Shells*. Whitaker and Ray Wiggins Co., San Francisco, 1911.

MacFarland, F. M.—*Opistobranchiate Mollusca from Monterey Bay, California, and Vicinity*. Bull. Bur. Fisheries, Vol. 25, 1906.

Mayer, Alfred—*Seashore Life*. New York Zoological Soc., 1911.

Newbegin, M. I.—*Life by the Seashore*. Geo Allen and Unwin, Ltd., London, 1931.

O'Donoghue, Chas. H.—*A note on the Polychaetous Annelid-Eudistylia Gigantea* (Bush). Contr. to Can. Biol., N. S., Vol. 1, 1924.

Oldroyd, Ida S.—*Marine Shells of Puget Sound and Vicinity*. Pub. Puget Sound Biol. Sta., Vol. 4, 1924.

Parker and Haswell—*A Text Book of Zoology*. Macmillan and Co., N. Y., 1897.

Pearse, A. S.—*Animal Ecology*. McGraw-Hill Co., N. Y., 1926.

Potts, F. A.—*The Chaetopteridae*. Polychaeta from the North East Pacific. Proc. of Zool. Soc., London, 1914.

Pratt, Henry—*Manual of the Common Invertebrate Animals*. McClurg and Co., Chicago, 1916.

Russell and Yonge—*The Seas*. Frederick Warne and Co. Ltd., London, 1928.

Stevens, Belle—*Hermit Crabs of Friday Harbor, Washington*. Pub. Puget Sound Biol. Sta., Vol. 3, 1925.

Stevens, Belle—*Callianassidae From West Coast of North America*. Pub. Puget Sound Bio. Sta., Vol. 6, 1928.

Thomson, J. Arthur—*Haunts of Life*. Harcourt, Brace and Co., N. Y., 1922.

Way, Evelyn—*Brachyura and Crab-like Anomura of Friday Harbor, Washington*. Pub. Puget Snd. Biol. Sta., Vol.1, 1917.

Woodward, B. B.—*The Life of the Mollusca*. Methuen & Co., Ltd., London, 1913.

INDEX

406

409

410